Electing Our President

Third Edition

by Nancy Gill

Good Apple

A Division of Frank Schaffer Publications, Inc.

Editorial Director: Kristin Eclov
Editor: Christine Hood
Illustrator: Don O'Connor
Inside Design: Riley Wilkinson
Cover Design: Riley Wilkinson
Production: Drew R. Moore

Good Apple
A Division of Frank Schaffer Publications, Inc.
23740 Hawthorne Boulevard
Torrance, CA 90505-5927

GA13053

Table of Contents

Introduction

THOMAS JEFFERSON, OUR COUNTRY'S THIRD PRESIDENT, described the job of being United States' president as "a splendid misery." When asked if he missed being president after his second term, Harry Truman, our 33rd president, said, "I'm glad to be rid of it. One really can't enjoy being president of the greatest republic in the history of the world. It's just too big a job for any one man to control it." Dwight Eisenhower, our 34th president, showed that he was looking forward to the end of his second term when he said, "Oh, that lovely title, ex-president."

Almost everyone would agree that being president of the United States is one of the most difficult jobs in the world. The road to election is almost as difficult as the job itself. Candidates must spend millions of dollars, shake thousands of hands, travel thousands of miles, and make hundreds of speeches to try to convince American voters that they are the best for the job. Despite the hardship of the job and the long, grueling process required to get elected, dozens of able Americans announce themselves as candidates for this "splendid misery."

Every four years, on the first Tuesday after the first Monday in November, millions of Americans go to neighborhood polls to cast their votes for the next president of the United States. Many other countries have democracies that allow citizens to choose their leaders. But probably no other country holds its elections with as much noise or hoopla as the United States.

This book is designed to draw students into the fascinating drama of our presidential election process. Too often, this most basic and interesting part of our historical and political heritage is ignored or skimmed over in our schools. Many adults, let alone students, have little understanding of how we actually elect our leaders.

This resource combines a step-by-step explanation of how we elect our presidents, including historical anecdotes that demonstrate how elections have changed throughout the years and how our colorful past has affected our present. Each reproducible informational passage is followed by an activity page designed to develop a variety of skills. These pages include review questions that develop skills across the curriculum in comprehension, vocabulary development, critical thinking, analyzing, math, and more.

Questions preceded by **one asterisk** ask students to give an opinion or use logical thinking skills. These questions are often open-ended. If you do not feel students are ready to answer these questions independently, you may want to use them for class discussion or assign them as homework, so students can discuss them with their parents. Questions preceded by **two asterisks** are research or project activities. You may wish to assign these as extra-credit assignments or as culminating activities for individual groups. Also watch for bold-face words throughout the passages; these are defined in a glossary at the back of the book, along with a variety of extension activity and project suggestions designed to give students a better understanding of our election process.

Introducing Presidential Elections

W HAT DO YOU REMEMBER ABOUT THE last presidential election campaign? You might have noticed the **candidates'** ads on television. You might have heard your parents and their friends discussing the candidates. But chances are you were too young to pay much attention.

You won't miss the next one, though. The presidential campaign is the most important political race in our country. Election day happens every four years—on the first Tuesday after the first Monday in November. But the race starts long before that day.

First, at least a year before election day, leading members of the political parties start to "toss their hats into the ring," announcing their plans to run for the presidency. Then, between February and June of election year, the Democratic and Republican party organizations in each state decide which candidates they'll support. In over 30 states, this decision is made in presidential preference **primaries**. **Registered** Democrats and Republicans vote for one of their party's candidates. The state party will support the winners of the primary election. In the remaining states, the state party's candidates are chosen by party caucuses or meetings of members.

In the summer, after the parties in each state have chosen their candidates, they send **delegates** to their party's national **convention**. Here, the state delegates vote to nominate the national party's candidate for president.

Once the national party **nominees** are chosen, the presidential campaign begins. Each nominee tries to convince the voters that he or she is the best candidate. The nominees want as many people as possible to see their faces and hear their ideas. To do this, they spend millions of dollars, shake thousands of hands, travel thousands of miles, and make hundreds of speeches.

Then on election day, millions of Americans go to neighborhood **polls** to cast their votes for the next president of the United States. After the election is over, the happy face of the victor appears on television screens and front pages of newspapers around the world. But there is still one more step before the winner of the

popular election is officially elected. That is the vote by the electoral college in December. Later in this book, you'll learn how it works. The electoral college vote must then be counted by Congress.

Finally, on January 20, the new president is **inaugurated** and begins a challenging four-year term as the holder of the highest office in our nation.

As you will soon see, the process of electing a president has not always been so complicated. It has changed during the 200 years that we have been holding presidential elections. The purpose of these changes has been to give more people a say in who their president will be. There are still discussions about whether the election process is truly a **democratic** one.

Name _____

★ How often are U.S. presidential elections held? _____

     On what day are they held? _____

★ Use the context (the words and/or sentences surrounding a particular word in text that help show its meaning) of the section or a dictionary to define the following words.

candidate _____

primary _____

nominee _____

polls _____

inaugurated _____

democratic _____

★ Number the following steps in the presidential election process in the order in which they happen.

    _____ electoral college meets

    _____ people "toss their hats into the ring"

    _____ inauguration day

    _____ national party nominating conventions

    _____ election day

    _____ state primaries or party conventions

* ★ In your opinion, what are some of the reasons a voter chooses one candidate over another?

_____

_____

** ★ Who have been the presidents during your lifetime? In what years were they elected?

_____

_____

** ★ When is the next presidential election? _____

reproducible

Our Constitution Defines the Presidency

IN THE SUMMER OF 1787, 55 DELEGATES to the Constitutional Convention met in Philadelphia. They faced an extremely difficult task—to write a constitution, a document that would set forth the laws and create the government of the new nation. Eleven years earlier, these men had supported the nation's independence from the king of England, so they did not want a new government in which one person could become too powerful.

Their solution was to set up three separate branches of government. Each branch would watch over the other two. **Congress, the legislative branch,** was to be made up of members from all the states. It was given the power to make laws. The **judiciary branch** was given the power to explain the laws through a system of courts and judges. The **executive branch** was assigned the power to execute, or carry out, the laws that Congress made. The head of the executive branch was to be called "president."

The Constitution gives the president three types of responsibilities:

1. **Legislative.** The president enforces the Constitution and the nation's laws. He or she also recommends measures to Congress and signs into law or vetoes bills passed by Congress.

2. **Diplomatic.** The president meets with leaders of other nations and makes treaties (with the consent of the **Senate**) with them.

3. **Military.** The president is commander in chief of the armed forces and can send troops into action anywhere in the world if American lives or interests seem to be in danger.

In addition, the president has the duty to appoint **cabinet** members, ambassadors, and federal judges (again, with the consent of the Senate).

The Constitution lists only three qualifications a person needs in order to be president. The president must (1) be at least 35 years old, (2) have lived in the United States at least 14 years, and (3) be a native-born citizen of this country.

The writers of the Constitution had great difficulty deciding how long a president should serve. Some wanted the president to serve 20-year terms; others thought a two-year term would be best. After much debate, they decided that presidents would serve four-year terms; however, no limit was placed on the number of times a president could be elected. But in 1951, an amendment to the Constitution set a limit of two terms in office for each president.

Each new president takes office by repeating the oath written in the Constitution some 200 years ago: "I do solemnly swear (or affirm) that I will faithfully execute the Office of the President of the United States, and will to the best of my ability, preserve, protect, and defend the Constitution of the United States."

Name _____

★1 Name the three branches of government set up by the Constitution, and briefly tell what each branch does.

    (1) _____

    (2) _____

    (3) _____

★2 List three duties the Constitution gives to the president of the United States.

    (1) _____

    (2) _____

    (3) _____

★3 The Constitution lists three qualifications needed to be president. First, the president must be a native-born citizen of the United States. What are the other two?

_____

_____

★4 How many four-year terms may a president serve? _____

★5 In the oath of office, which document does the president pledge to "preserve, protect, and defend"?

_____

*★6 What would be the advantages and disadvantages of having presidents serve 20-year terms?

_____

_____

*★7 Why do you think the Constitution requires a person to have reached a certain age before becoming president? Do you think age is important?

_____

_____

**★8 In 1951, an amendment to the Constitution set a limit on the number of terms a president may serve. Find out why this amendment was passed.

_____

_____

The Electoral College

DID YOU KNOW THAT VOTERS IN THE United States don't vote for the president? When they go to the polls on election day, they are actually voting for a group of electors. These electors have pledged to support a party's nominee for president. Many people believe they are voting for the president, because in many states the **ballot** lists only the names of the nominees and not the names of the electors.

The delegates to the Constitutional Convention in 1787 decided on this system of **indirect election** of the president. They had long debates about how to make sure that the best candidate would be chosen as president. Some delegates supported a **direct election** by citizens. Others were in favor of having Congress choose the president. And still others thought that state legislatures should make the choice.

The delegates finally agreed on a **compromise**—the president would be elected by electors chosen by each state. This way, ordinary citizens in each state would have a say, but the final decision would be made by people who were better informed about the candidates and the issues.

This system of presidential electors, called the **electoral college**, is still in effect today. But some adjustments have been made over the years. At first, the electors voted for two candidates. The one with the highest number of votes became president, and the one with the second-highest number became vice president. But in 1796, political foes were chosen for the two posts—Federalist John Adams for president and Democratic-Republican Thomas Jefferson for vice president. In the next election, there was a tie between Thomas Jefferson and Aaron Burr. The **House of Representatives** had to decide who would be president. It was clear that the system needed to be adjusted. In 1804, the 12th Amendment to the Constitution was passed. Candidates are now nominated to run only for president or only for vice president. Electors vote for president and vice president separately.

There have been changes in how the states elect electors, too. In the beginning, some states held direct

popular elections for the electors. In others, the state legislatures made the choice. Gradually, all the states adopted direct popular elections for electors.

When the Constitution was written, there were no political parties. But they soon developed, and the party organizations in each state began proposing a **slate,** or list, of electors who were pledged to vote for their party's nominee. Voters no longer chose individual electors; they chose between party slates.

Political parties then began to push for **winner-take-all elections** for electors. This meant that the slate that received the most popular votes won all the state's electoral votes. Today, all the states except Maine use this winner-take-all system.

The Electoral College

Name _____

⭐ Do voters in the United States vote directly for the president? _____

⭐ Fill in the blanks in the following sentences.

    a. The group of people who cast the official votes to elect the president and vice president
       is called the _____.

    b. A (an) _____ election is when the citizens vote for electors who elect
       the president.

    c. A (an) _____ election is when the citizens vote for the president.

    d. A (an) _____ election is when the winner of the popular election gets
       all of the state's electoral votes.

⭐ What did the 12th Amendment to the Constitution do?

_____

⭐ Today, all of the states but Maine have _____ elections to elect presidential electors.

    a. indirect   d. winner-take-all

    b. direct   e. *b* and *c*

    c. popular   f. all of the above

* ⭐ Many delegates to the Constitutional Convention believed that ordinary citizens were not well-enough informed to choose the best candidate for president. In your opinion, were they right or wrong? Explain your answer.

_____

_____

_____

** ⭐ The House of Representatives has twice had to choose a president. One was Thomas Jefferson. Who was the other?

_____

                           reproducible

The Electoral Map

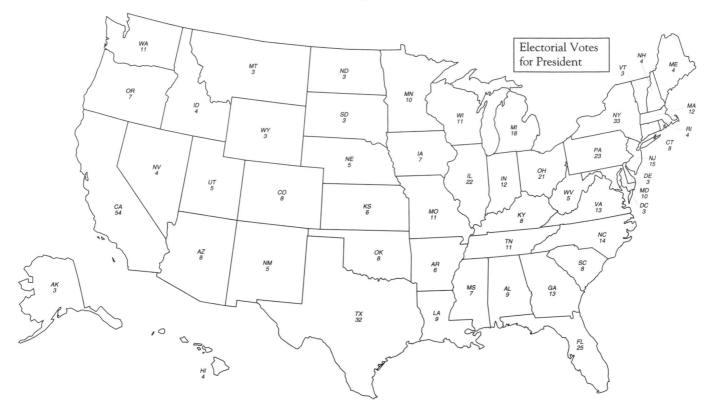

Electoral Votes for President

T O WIN THE PRESIDENCY, A NOMINEE needs a majority of the electoral votes. On election night, you'll notice that the TV commentators keep track of the states each nominee wins. They add up the number of electoral votes that each state win represents. As soon as one of the nominees gets one more than half of the total of electoral votes, the race is over.

The nation usually knows the winner of the election on election night or early the next morning. However, the president is not officially elected until the members of the electoral college cast their state's votes in December, and Congress counts those votes on January 6.

When George Washington was elected, there were just 13 states and only 69 electoral votes. Our nation has grown a lot since then, and today there are 538 electoral votes. But the number of electors each state has is still determined the way it was in Washington's day. The Constitution allows each state to have as many electoral votes as it has representatives in Congress. The number of representatives depends on the size of the state's population. Because each state has two **senators** and at least one **representative** in the House of Representatives,

no state has fewer than three electoral votes.

Every ten years, at the beginning of every decade, the government takes a census to determine the population of each state. If a state's population has decreased, it might lose electoral votes. If a state's population has increased, it may receive more electoral votes than it previously had. The electoral map above was drawn up after the 1990 census.

Over the years, many have criticized the electoral college system. Some attempts to change it have been successful, as you saw in the previous section. But two important criticisms still remain unanswered. First, there is no guarantee that an elector who is pledged to vote for a certain candidate will actually do so. Only a few electors have switched their vote, however, and none changed the outcome of an election. The second criticism is about the winner-take-all system. A nominee can get all of a state's electoral votes by getting just one more popular vote than the opponent. Because of this system, three nominees have been elected president even though their opponents received more popular votes nationally.

Name _____

⭐ 1 How many electoral votes does a nominee need in order to win the presidency?

_____

⭐ 2 What are the five states with the highest number of electoral votes?

_____

What is the total number of electoral votes of these five states? _____

⭐ 3 How many electoral votes does your state have? _____

How many senators? _____ How many representatives? _____

⭐ 4 A class of sixth graders is having an election using the electoral college system. They have divided themselves into four "states." Refer to the chart to answer the questions.

State	No. of Citizens	No. of Electors	Votes for Justin	Votes for Mia
Minnesota	15	10	7	8
Kentucky	9	8	4	5
Idaho	6	4	5	1
Alaska	3	3	2	1

a. Why does Minnesota get more electoral votes than Idaho?

_____

b. How many popular votes did Mia win? _____

c. How many electoral votes does she get? _____

d. How many popular votes did Justin win? _____

e. How many electoral votes does Justin get? _____

f. Who won the election? _____

⭐ 5 In your opinion, is the electoral college a good way to elect a president? Explain your answer on a separate sheet of paper.

⭐ 6 Which three presidents were elected by the electoral college even though they had fewer popular votes than their opponents?

_____

© Good Apple GA13053   reproducible

Who Can Vote?

IN THE EARLY DAYS OF OUR NATION, approximately four out of five adults were not eligible to vote. Today, nearly every citizen who is 18 or older can vote. The writers of the Constitution allowed the states to determine who could vote. Most states allowed only white males over 21 who owned property to vote. Women, African Americans, Native Americans, and white males who did not own property were not allowed to vote in either state or federal elections.

Today, the people who cast votes in our country's elections include men and women from all economic, racial, and religious groups. The **electorate** has expanded because the Constitution has been amended several times.

- The 14th Amendment was **ratified** in 1868, just after the Civil War. It said that any eligible 21-year-old male had the right to vote. They could vote even if they did not own property.

- The 15th Amendment was ratified two years later, in 1870. It said that the right to vote cannot be denied "on account of race, color, or previous condition of servitude." Now men of color, as well as white men over 21, could vote.

- The 19th Amendment was ratified in 1920. Until that time, few states allowed women to vote. This amendment said that the right to vote cannot be denied "on account of sex."

- The 23rd Amendment was ratified in 1961. It gave the citizens of the District of Columbia the right to vote for electors in presidential and vice-presidential elections. Although it has as many people as some states, the District of Columbia is not a state. The early leaders of our nation established this federal district. Because there had been much disagreement about which state would be the site of the nation's capital, they decided to put it on land that did not belong to any state.

- The 24th Amendment was ratified in 1964. It declared that the states could not require citizens

to pay a **poll tax** in order to vote in federal elections. Some states had instituted this tax in the 1890s. Many people believed that it was aimed at poor people, especially poor African Americans, to keep them from voting.

- The 26th Amendment was ratified in 1971. It lowered the voting age to 18 for national, state, and local elections. In the 1960s, during the Vietnam War, many Americans complained that 18-, 19-, and 20-year-olds were considered old enough to fight and die for our country, but were not old enough to vote in most states. This amendment was ratified in response to this complaint.

Today, the only people who are not eligible to vote are those who have been convicted of a felony and those who are severely mentally disturbed. Otherwise, all citizens who are at least 18 years of age have the right to vote in the United States. Unfortunately, many eligible voters do not choose to vote. During the 1970s and early 1980s, only 50–55% of the electorate voted in presidential elections. Thus, Jimmy Carter was elected president by only 27% of America's qualified voters, and Ronald Reagan by only 28%.

Name _____

★1 Place a checkmark by those groups of citizens who could vote in 1800.

_____ wives of property owners   _____ Native Americans

_____ free blacks   _____ white men over 21 who owned property

_____ white men over 21 who did not own property

★2 Use the context of the section or a dictionary to define the following terms.

electorate _____

ratified _____

poll tax _____

★3 Match the amendment with the group to which it gave the vote.

_____ 14th Amendment   a. women

_____ 15th Amendment   b. residents of Washington, D.C.

_____ 19th Amendment   c. white men who don't own property

_____ 23rd Amendment   d. 18- to 20-year-olds

_____ 26th Amendment   e. men of color over 21

★4 Which three groups of U.S. citizens are not eligible to vote today?

_____

*★5 In your opinion, should there be any restrictions on the right to vote? Explain your answer.

_____

_____

*★6 In 1960, 63% of eligible voters voted, but in 1996, only 49% voted, reflecting a steady decline in voter turnout over the last 36 years. Why do you think this is the case?

_____

_____

**★7 What were some of the events in the 1960s that may have influenced the decision to lower the voting age to 18?

_____

_____

reproducible

The Struggle for Women's Suffrage

THE STRUGGLE TO WIN WOMEN THE vote lasted over 100 years. Although this struggle had many setbacks, those who led the **suffrage** movement carried on with courage and determination.

When the Constitution was written, women had few rights. Married women were not allowed to own property or sign contracts. Everything a woman had, including inherited property and her children, belonged to her husband. The Constitution gave states the right to determine who could vote. Because many felt women were "mentally inferior," none of the states chose to grant them the vote.

In the early 1800s, women began to question why a country built on equality did not allow half of its population to vote. In 1848, the first of hundreds of women's conventions met in Seneca Falls, New York. The convention issued a Declaration of Sentiments, which called for women to have equal rights in education, property, and voting. The people involved in this campaign were called **suffragists.** Although most newspapers "jeered" at the Seneca Convention, the publicity surrounding it helped the movement spread.

During the Civil War, many suffragists worked to help end slavery and win the vote for African Americans. However, after the war they were greatly disappointed when voting rights were given to white men who did not own property, and with the passing of the 15th Amendment, African American men as well.

Though suffragists had failed to win the vote on a national level, they began to see success in individual states. In 1869, the territory of Wyoming gave women the right to vote in its elections. When Wyoming applied for statehood, Congress asked it to **disenfranchise** its women. Wyoming refused. This thinly populated state needed voters. Soon Colorado, Idaho, Utah, and Indiana extended the vote to women.

In 1878, Congress was asked to consider an amendment (known as the Anthony Amendment, named for Susan B. Anthony) to the Constitution that would give women the right to vote. But Congress did not pass it. During the next 42 years, more people joined the campaign to give women the vote. They marched in

parades, held demonstrations, and tried to vote. They were often attacked by spectators and arrested by police. Many suffragists were treated unfairly and put in jail.

By 1900, a new generation of college-educated women, combined with the growing number of working women, gave new energy to the suffrage movement. A few more states awarded women the vote, but suffragists continued to be defeated at the national level.

During World War I (1914–1918), women made many important contributions to the war effort. Although he was impressed by their help in winning the war, President Wilson was still staunchly opposed to the women's vote. But the protests and pressure were becoming unbearable. Some women had even protested in front of the Capitol and chained themselves to the gates. Wilson could no longer ignore the suffragists. He finally asked Congress to pass the amendment, which took two more years to pass through Congress.

By the summer of 1920, only one more state was needed to ratify the amendment to make it part of the Constitution. The amendment was before the Tennessee legislature, and lawmakers were divided on the issue. Finally, one young legislator cast the deciding vote. He explained, "A mother's advice is always the safest for her boy to follow, and my mother wants me to vote for ratification." After a long struggle, the 19th Amendment had been ratified. Women had finally won the right to vote.

© Good Apple GA13053

Name _____

★1 Circle the true statements.

   a. The Constitution originally stated that women could not vote.

   b. The first convention for women's rights occurred in 1848.

   c. The western states were the most reluctant to give women the vote.

   d. President Wilson ran for office supporting women's suffrage.

   e. Many women suffragists were against slavery.

★2 How many years did it take for this amendment to be ratified after it was first introduced in Congress?

_____

★3 What did the Declaration of Sentiments call for?

_____

_____

★4 Match the event with the state in which it took place.

   _____ New York   a. the final vote to ratify the 19th Amendment

   _____ Wyoming   b. women were given the vote in 1869

   _____ Tennessee   c. the beginning of the women's suffrage movement

*★5 Why do you think college-educated women and women working outside the home were especially active in the women's suffrage movement?

_____

_____

*★6 State some of the arguments that you think might have been given by anti-suffragists, the people who were against letting women vote.

_____

_____

**★7 Research the life of one of the following leaders of the suffragist movement: Susan B. Anthony, Lucretia Mott, Elizabeth Cady Stanton, Sojourner Truth, Carrie Chapman Catt.

Political Parties

THERE IS NO MENTION OF **POLITICAL parties** in the Constitution; however, they started to appear during George Washington's term of office. The Federalists wanted a strong federal government; the Democratic-Republicans believed that the power of the federal government should be limited. Their leader was Thomas Jefferson, who became the third president of the United States.

Washington, however, was opposed to political parties. He feared that they would divide the nation. In his farewell address, he warned that "the common and continual mischief of the spirit of party . . . agitates the community with ill-founded jealousies and false alarms, [and] kindles the animosity of one part against another."

Nevertheless, political parties continue to exist and prove to be an effective way for people with similar ideas about public issues to work together. It is hard to imagine how an election would work without them. Political parties hold the nominating conventions and select the candidates. Their members raise money and work hard to get votes for their candidates.

Several of the early political parties have long disappeared—like the Federalists and the Whigs. Since 1854, the two major parties have been the Republican party and the Democratic party. (The Democratic party grew out of Jefferson's Democratic-Republican party.)

Throughout history, there have also been a number of smaller parties, which usually lasted only a short time. These are known as **third parties.** Many of them had colorful names, like the Greenback party, the Free Soil party, the Know-Nothings, and the "Bull Moose" party. A few third-party candidates have attracted a number of voters.

Anyone can join a political party. When people register to vote, they usually declare their party preference. Millions of Americans register as Democrats or Republicans, but many say they are **"independent."** Only a small number of the people who are registered as members of a party take an active role in party activities. In most primary elections, party members must vote for their party's candidates. In general elections, they can vote for candidates of any party. When the member of one party votes for the candidate of another party, it is called a **crossover vote.**

Each party is organized into committees at the neighborhood level, at the city level, at the county level, at the state level, and at the national level. These committees work to get their party's candidates elected to office. At election time, **rank-and-file** members work in their party's headquarters to get out the vote. They call neighbors to promote their candidate. They hand out flyers about their candidate. They even drive people to polling places so they can vote.

Political Parties

Name _____

⭐1 What are the names of the two major political parties in the United States?

_____

⭐2 The smaller political parties are usually called _____ parties.

⭐3 People who don't want to register as a member of a political party can register as

_____.

⭐4 Do people who are registered as members of a political party always have to vote for that party's

candidate? _____

⭐5 Name three things that active party members do during a campaign to get votes for their
candidate.

_____

_____

_____

⭐6 Why was George Washington opposed to political parties?

_____

**⭐7 The Democratic party grew out of Thomas Jefferson's Democratic-Republican party. Find out
how and when the Republican party began. Describe its origin on a separate sheet of paper.

**⭐8 Use the encyclopedia to find out what one of the following third parties stood for: Prohibition
party, Progressive party, Greenback party, Free Soil party, Know-Nothing party, or "Bull Moose"
party. Write your findings on a separate sheet of paper.

**⭐9 Interview two adults—one Republican and one Democrat. Find out why each prefers his or her
party.

reproducible

The Long Road to Victory

ANY AMERICAN CAN RUN FOR PRESIDENT if he or she meets the three qualifications set forth in the Constitution. But the people who win their party's nomination usually have one more qualification. They have held government positions. Most nominees have already served as governor, senator, or vice president. **Incumbent** presidents often have a good chance of being reelected. They have already served one term as president, so the voters know and trust them. Sixteen of our presidents have been reelected for second terms.

We elect a president every four years. But that is only the last step in a long process. The steps in the campaign process usually include the following:

1. **Announce candidacy.** Candidates officially announce that they are running for their party's nomination the year before the election year. Before they make this announcement, they talk to many people. They want to be sure they have a chance to win. As soon as one election is over, likely candidates for the next election begin to line up support.

2. **Campaign for the party nomination.** During this stage, candidates from the same party compete for their party's nomination. The heaviest campaigning for the nomination happens during late winter and spring of election year.

3. **Win the nomination.** Each political party holds a nominating convention in July or August of election year. Each state sends delegates to the convention to vote for the person they want as the party's candidate. After the presidential nominee is chosen, the convention chooses a nominee for vice president.

4. **Campaign for election.** Each party's nominees for president and vice president start campaigning around Labor Day. They travel across the country to meet as many people as possible. They appear in the media as often as they can. A month or two before the election, the presidential nominees may **debate** each other on television. The reason for all

this campaigning is to convince the voters that they will make the best president.

5. **Win the election.** On election day, the nominees find out if their months of hard work paid off. Television and radio stations broadcast the results that come in from each state. If the vote is a **landslide**, the winner will be announced soon after the polls close. If the election is close, the winner may not be declared until the next day.

© Good Apple GA13053

Name _____

⭐**1** What is the fourth unofficial qualification that someone usually needs to be elected president?

_____

⭐**2** Use the context of the section or a dictionary to define the following words.

incumbent _____

debate _____

landslide _____

⭐**3** In the time line below, label the steps of the presidential campaign process. The last step has been labeled for you.

				← Election Day

Jan   Feb   Mar   Apr   May   June   July   Aug   Sept   Oct   Nov   Dec

——————— **Election Year** ———————

⭐**4** Which stage of the presidential campaign process is our country in right now?

_____

*⭐**5** In your opinion, could someone make a good president who has not held a government office before? Explain your answer.

_____

_____

⭐6** To what other government offices were these recent presidents elected?

Ronald Reagan _____

Jimmy Carter _____

Richard Nixon _____

John Kennedy _____

Dwight Eisenhower _____

George Bush _____

Bill Clinton _____

reproducible

Presidential Primaries: The Race Is On!

PRESIDENTIAL PREFERENCE PRIMARIES allow voters to show which candidate they prefer. Their votes are then represented at the national conventions that nominate the parties' candidates for president. Presidential primaries are not actual elections. They serve to measure party support for the candidates.

Until about 1900, there were no primary elections. The Constitution does not specify how presidents should be nominated. During the 1800s, presidential candidates were nominated by delegates at party conventions. The delegates were chosen by the party leaders of states and big cities. These leaders were sometimes called **party bosses.** Ordinary voters had no say in naming their parties' presidential nominees.

At the turn of the century, some people began calling for more say in the political process. These people were part of the progressive movement. They did not want the parties to be run by the party bosses. First in Florida in 1901, then in Wisconsin and Pennsylvania, and then in many other states, presidential primaries were established. Ordinary citizens could then vote for the delegates they wanted for party conventions. In 1996, 41 states held presidential primaries, as well as Washington D.C. and Puerto Rico.

Many states now hold presidential primaries so voters can have a say in who their party's candidate will be. There are two kinds of primaries—closed and open. The **closed primary** allows only registered Democrats to vote for Democrats and only registered Republicans to vote for Republicans. Some states have an **open primary.** This kind of election allows voters to decide on election day whether they want to vote on the Democratic or Republican ballot. In recent years, many states have moved their primaries so they occur earlier. For example, California used to hold its primary during the first week of June, but in 2000, its presidential primary will be held on March 7.

Primaries take place during the late winter and spring of election year. Presidential candidates spend a great deal of time and money campaigning in states with primaries. Winning primaries is important for two

reasons. First, a primary victory shows that the candidate is popular. This makes it easier to raise money to continue campaigning. Candidates who do not win any primaries usually drop out of the race. Second, a primary victory gives the candidate some delegates at the nominating convention.

Some state primaries are more important than others. Candidates want to win the primaries in big states like New York and California that send a large number of delegates to the conventions. Although New Hampshire is one of the smallest states, its primary is important, too. It holds the first primary in the election year. The Republican and Democratic winners in the New Hampshire primary are usually serious contenders in the race.

Presidential Primaries: The Race Is On!

Name _____

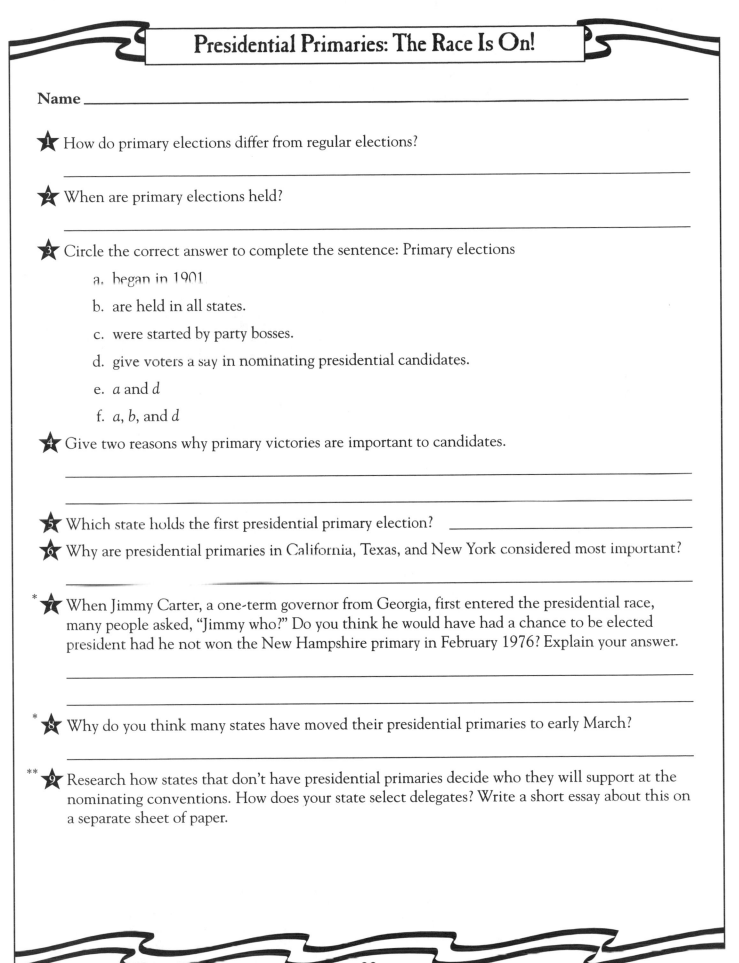

⭐ **1** How do primary elections differ from regular elections?

_____

⭐ **2** When are primary elections held?

_____

⭐ **3** Circle the correct answer to complete the sentence: Primary elections

     a. began in 1901

     b. are held in all states.

     c. were started by party bosses.

     d. give voters a say in nominating presidential candidates.

     e. *a* and *d*

     f. *a*, *b*, and *d*

⭐ **4** Give two reasons why primary victories are important to candidates.

_____

_____

⭐ **5** Which state holds the first presidential primary election? _____

⭐ **6** Why are presidential primaries in California, Texas, and New York considered most important?

_____

* ⭐ **7** When Jimmy Carter, a one-term governor from Georgia, first entered the presidential race, many people asked, "Jimmy who?" Do you think he would have had a chance to be elected president had he not won the New Hampshire primary in February 1976? Explain your answer.

_____

_____

* ⭐ **8** Why do you think many states have moved their presidential primaries to early March?

_____

** ⭐ **9** Research how states that don't have presidential primaries decide who they will support at the nominating conventions. How does your state select delegates? Write a short essay about this on a separate sheet of paper.

reproducible

Nominating Conventions: The Delegates

WHEN ABRAHAM LINCOLN WAS nominated at 1860's Republican party convention, one observer compared the scene to "all the hogs ever slaughtered in Cincinnati giving their death squeals together." This observation illustrates why many consider America's presidential nominating conventions the most interesting and colorful part of the election process.

Balloons, banners, and funny hats; big signposts splashed with state names; posters and buttons printed with candidates' names and pictures. This "party" is a presidential nominating convention for the Republican or Democratic party. Each party holds its national convention during the summer of election year.

Delegates come from the 50 states, Washington, D.C., Puerto Rico, and the Virgin Islands to choose their party's nominees for president and vice president. They also adopt a party **platform,** a statement of the party's goals and views on important domestic and foreign policy issues. Delegates do not all come to the convention supporting the same candidate, nor do they come with the same ideas about what each **plank** of the platform should contain. In the process of deciding on the nominees and the platform, they must compromise. Making these decisions helps unite the party.

In the 19th century, location was considered the most important factor in selecting a convention site. Chicago was the most popular city because it is located in America's heartland. However, as transportation improved, location was no longer an important issue. Today, political parties consider other factors, such as who will pledge financial support and provide adequate services and facilities, such as auditoriums and hotels to house thousands of delegates, family members, reporters, and spectators.

The Constitution does not describe how to nominate presidents. Our early presidents were nominated by secret congressional **caucuses.** Party nominating conventions are a **tradition** that has grown out of experience. The first national nominating convention was held by the Anti-Masonic party in 1831. Only 116 delegates from 13 states attended the convention of this small third party. Today, about 3,000 delegates come to

the national conventions of the two major parties.

When parties first started to hold national nominating conventions, there was no formal system for selecting delegates. At the Democratic convention in 1835, Maryland had 188 delegates to cast the state's ten votes. Tennessee's 15 votes were cast by a traveling businessman who happened to be in town at the time.

Today, each state has a formal process for choosing delegates. In some states, they are chosen by a primary election. In others, they are chosen by a party caucus. Each national party committee decides how many delegates each state may send to the national convention. This formula has changed over the years. Today, each state can send twice as many delegates as the total number of senators and representatives it has in Congress. A state may send additional delegates if the party's candidate won in that state in the last presidential election. These bonus delegates are a reward for the hard work of state parties. Each state also sends alternates in case any regular delegate becomes ill.

Most of the delegates are pledged to support a certain candidate in the first round of voting. They are called **committed delegates.** The number of delegates for each candidate is usually based on the percentage of votes for that candidate in the primary. There are also a small number of **uncommitted delegates.** They can vote for any candidate they wish.

Name _____

★1 The delegates and candidates at a nominating convention are all from the same

_____ .

★2 What are the two most important decisions made at a national nominating convention?

_____

_____

★3 Use the context of the section or a dictionary to define the following words.

platform _____

plank _____

tradition _____

★4 Minnesota has two senators and eight representatives. If the Republican candidate does not win the majority of votes in that state in the last election, how many regular delegates can Minnesota send to the next Republican convention?

_____

*★5 National nominating conventions are sometimes referred to as the biggest rallies of the campaign. In your opinion, should the nomination of presidential candidates be more solemn and formal? Explain why or why not.

_____

_____

_____

*★6 Modern conventions are not as raucous as they once were. Explain why you think convention delegates behave less wildly than they once did.

_____

_____

**★7 What is the minimum number of delegates the Republican and Democratic parties in your state will be able to send to their next national nominating conventions?

_____

Which party will be able to send bonus delegates?

_____

reproducible

Nominating Conventions: The Events

ONE OBSERVER AT THE 1884 REPUBLICAN national convention described the uproar after James G. Blaine's name was put on the convention ballot.

Whole delegations mounted their chairs and led the cheering, which instantly spread to the stage and deepened into a roar fully as deep and deafening as the voice of the Niagara. . . . The air quivered, the gaslights trembled, and the walls fairly shook. . . . Hats, umbrellas, handkerchiefs, and other personal belongings were tossed to and fro like bubbles over the great sea of human heads.

Similar scenes can be seen at nominating conventions today. These series of events are much like those of conventions 100 years ago.

On the first day of a national nominating convention, the chairperson calls the convention to order. The chairperson is a prominent party member who has already been selected by the party's national committee. Next, the **keynote speaker** gives an opening speech to both the delegates and the television and radio audience. Many politicians have made themselves known to the whole nation by giving an eloquent keynote address.

Then, the convention votes on the rules of procedure for the convention as well as the party platform. Both of these have been drafted beforehand by committees. If some delegates disagree with the recommended platform, there may be a lively debate.

Next comes the most important task of the convention—the nomination of the presidential candidate. The nomination begins with a roll call of the states. As each state is called, it can put in a name for nomination. Usually a prominent supporter gives the nominating speech, praising the candidate as the party's best choice. After this speech, the candidate's supporters participate in a long, noisy demonstration—like that for James G. Blaine in 1884. They parade around the convention hall, waving banners and signs, cheering, and blowing horns. In 1908, the demonstration following the nomination of William Jennings Bryan at the Democratic convention lasted an hour and a half.

However, now that conventions are televised, demonstrations are much briefer. Once things quiet down, other supporters give **seconding speeches.** These show additional support for the candidate.

After each state has had an opportunity to make a nomination, the voting begins. States are called in alphabetical order, and a delegate from each state announces how the state will cast its vote.

To win the nomination, a candidate must receive a majority of delegate votes. At many conventions, a candidate wins easily on the first ballot. This candidate has come into the convention as the **front-runner.** A president running for reelection is almost always the front-runner. If the president is not running again, the leading candidate is usually the one who has won the most support in primaries and state caucuses. Since 1952, neither party has taken more than one ballot to nominate its candidate.

When a state's delegation announces the vote that puts a candidate **"over the top,"** the delegates cheer enthusiastically to demonstrate their support for the party's presidential nominee.

Name _____

⭐ Number the events in the order in which they happen in a nominating convention.

_____ keynote speech

_____ state roll call for nominations

_____ committees draft recommended platform and convention rules

_____ delegates vote on party platform

states vote for presidential candidates

_____ the convention is called to order

⭐ Use the context of the section or a dictionary to define the following terms.

keynote speaker _____

seconding speech _____

front-runner_____

over the top _____

⭐ Mark the following statements true (T) or false (F).

_____ Nominating conventions are very orderly, dignified events.

_____ Political parties almost always renominate presidents who wish to run for reelection.

_____ The candidate who wins the most votes on the first ballot always wins the nomination.

⭐ The delegates who answer the roll call for their state's vote often say something like "Mr. (or Madam) chairperson, the great state of _____, home of _____, and known around the world for its _____, casts its votes for _____."

How would you fill in the blanks if you had this opportunity to boast about your state?

⭐ Why do you think party leaders now place time limits on demonstrations and speeches by state delegations?

_____

⭐ Who were the Republican and Democratic nominees for president and vice president in:

1960? _____

1972? _____

1988? _____

1992? _____

1996? _____

reproducible

Notable Nominating Conventions

THE REPUBLICAN PARTY HELD ONE OF its most interesting nominating conventions in 1880. Many delegates supported General Ulysses S. Grant, the national Civil War hero, who had already served as president between 1869 and 1877. They persuaded him to run for a third term. Grant's chief rival was James G. Blaine, a senator from Maine. On the first 35 ballots, Grant led, but he could not win a majority of votes. The convention was hopelessly **deadlocked** over the two candidates. To break the deadlock, Blaine's delegates changed their votes to a **"dark-horse"** candidate named James A. Garfield, a little-known senator from Ohio. Enough other delegates switched their votes to Garfield to give him the nomination on the 36th ballot.

The longest Democratic convention occurred during a heat wave in New York City in 1924. When the convention began, Alfred E. Smith, the popular New York governor, and California's William McAdoo were the front-runners. In ballot after ballot, the candidates remained deadlocked. Neither was able to win the two-thirds majority then required by the Democrats to win the nomination. Neither candidate was willing to withdraw. The delegates began to think they would be trapped in the convention hall forever. Tempers flared, and there were even fistfights. Finally, on the ninth day of the stalemate, McAdoo and Smith released their delegates. On the 103rd ballot, the exhausted Democrats turned to John W. Davis, a little-known lawyer from New York who had never served in an elective office. While there was little enthusiasm for their candidate, the delegates were greatly relieved to end their balloting marathon.

While the 1924 Democratic convention was the longest in history, the 1968 convention was the most violent. The United States was in the middle of the Vietnam War, the most unpopular war in the nation's history. When the Democrats met in Chicago in late August, the convention delegates were sharply divided between two groups. The "hawks" supported Vice President Hubert Humphrey. They thought the United States should gradually pull out of the war. The "doves"

supported Senator Eugene McCarthy, who wanted bombing in Vietnam stopped immediately. Humphrey easily won nomination on the first ballot. This made the anti-war Democrats very bitter. They put on black armbands and sang protest songs on the convention floor.

Outside the convention hall, the scene became more violent. Anti-war protesters had come to Chicago from all over the country, and they were angry about Humphrey's nomination. Chicago's mayor barricaded the convention hall and called in thousands of police to keep order. The demonstrators shouted and threw garbage at the police. These small clashes turned into a major battle as police responded by clubbing protesters and throwing tear gas. The bloody scene was captured on television, shocking viewers across the nation.

Name _____

★ Use the context of the section or a dictionary to define the following words.

deadlock _____

dark horse _____

★ Complete the crossword puzzle using the numbered clues.

Across

2. person who is running for office

3. meeting of delegates from a political party

7. highest elected official in the United States

8. part of 7 Down

10. A seconding _____ follows a candidate's nomination.

Down

1. piece of paper used in voting

4. what many people do on election day

5. select someone to run for public office

6. someone given the authority to act for others

7. statement of a national party's goals

8. Democrats are members of a _____.

9. One of the first events in a convention is a _____ speech.

** ★ Did Garfield become president in 1880? _____

Did Davis become president in 1924? _____

Did Humphrey become president in 1968? _____

** ★ What popular Democratic anti-war candidate was assassinated the night he won the 1968 California primary? _____

** ★ Interview someone who is at least 50 years old about his or her memories of the 1968 Democratic convention.

The Running Mate

JOHN NANCE GARNER, A TWO-TERM vice president, wrote, "The vice presidency isn't worth a bucket of warm spit." In comparison to the president, the vice president has little to do. The Constitution assigns the vice president only one responsibility—to preside over the Senate. It is up to the president to give the vice president other duties.

Although the vice president doesn't have many official duties, politicians know that holding that office can lead to the most important office in the country—the presidency. About one-third of United States' vice presidents have become presidents. Five were elected president after serving full terms as vice president. One became president when the president resigned. Nine vice presidents became presidents when the presidents died in office, and four of those nine were then elected president in their own right. For this reason, it is often said that the vice president is "only a heartbeat away from the presidency."

The vice presidential nominee is selected by the national convention after it has chosen the presidential nominee. The presidential nominee usually chooses his or her running mate, but delegates must approve the choice. Most vice presidential nominees are chosen because they will balance the ticket. This means they have what the presidential nominee lacks. They may be from a different part of the country, have a different background, or appeal to a different group of voters. The purpose of a balanced ticket is to appeal to as many voters as possible.

In 1976, for example, Jimmy Carter, a southerner who had not held a federal office, chose Walter Mondale, a popular senator from the Midwest. When Mondale became the presidential nominee, he chose Geraldine Ferraro as his running mate. The Democrats hoped that having a woman on the ticket would win them a large number of women voters.

Another reason why a particular running mate is chosen is party unity. Restoring unity to the party is important if there have been close contests in the primaries and for the nomination. In this case, the runner-up for the

presidential nomination is often picked as the vice presidential nominee. This happened in 1960 when John Kennedy picked Lyndon Johnson. It happened again in 1980 when Ronald Reagan chose George Bush.

Thomas Marshall once said, "Once there were two brothers. One ran away to sea; the other was elected vice president, and nothing was ever heard from either of them again." This statement reflects a popular view of the vice presidency, but it is not entirely true. The vice president can help win votes for the president. And, even more important, he or she has a good chance of one day becoming president of the United States.

Name _____

★1 Mark the following statements true (T) or false (F).

_____ The national nominating convention has no role in deciding on the vice presidential nominee.

_____ Most vice presidential duties are decided on by the president.

★2 What does *balance the ticket* mean?

_____

★3 What is the purpose of balancing the ticket?

_____

_____

★4 What job does the Constitution assign to the vice president?

_____

*★5 Do you think the current president and vice president make a balanced ticket? Explain your answer.

_____

_____

_____

_____

*★6 Which nine vice presidents were elected president?

_____

_____

_____

**★7 Which vice president became president in 1974 when the acting president resigned?

_____

The History of Campaigning

Until about 100 years ago, it was considered undignified for presidential candidates to travel around the country campaigning for themselves. Instead, candidates stayed at home while supporters held rallies and parades to build support for them. In the 1860 election, Abraham Lincoln's opponent, Stephen A. Douglas, broke this tradition. He **took the stump** on his own behalf and became the first presidential candidate to make a nationwide trip to win votes. Many newspapers criticized him. One wrote, "Douglas is going about peddling his opinions as a tinman peddles his wares . . . strolling around the country begging for votes like a town constable."

But personal campaigning caught on. By 1869, the **transcontinental railroad line** was completed. Candidates could now travel to every state. Not until 1896, however, did a candidate make full use of the railroads. In this election campaign, William Jennings Bryan traveled over 18,000 miles by rail and made more than 600 speeches. His campaign train stopped at hundreds of small towns. Bryan spoke at each of these "whistle stops" from the train's rear platform. While Bryan traveled to 27 states, his opponent, William McKinley, stayed at home and greeted over 750,000 visitors from his front porch.

Although Bryan lost the election, his style of campaigning became popular. In the elections that followed, **whistle-stop campaigns** became the rule. All presidential candidates toured the country to sell themselves to the nation's voters.

Soon, other inventions changed the way candidates campaigned. A first occurred in 1924, when candidates used radio to make speeches to the nation. The Democratic convention was also broadcast. By 1928, in the race between Herbert Hoover and Alfred E. Smith, radio had become an integral vehicle for candidates to speak directly to large numbers of voters.

The airplane and television have also had a dramatic effect on our elections. In 1952, Dwight Eisenhower and Adlai Stevenson both used airplanes for most of their campaign travel. They did not have to spend time speaking at all the small whistle stops between big cities.

Soon, candidates realized that they could reach even more voters through television. Today, a major portion of each candidate's campaign budget is spent on television advertisements.

© Good Apple GA13053

Name _____

⭐ **1** Mark the following statements true (T) or false (F).

_____ Throughout United States' history, presidential candidates have always actively campaigned for themselves.

_____ Presidential candidates like to use television to reach voters because television advertising is free.

_____ New inventions have helped change the way politicians campaign.

⭐ **2** Use the context of the section or a dictionary to define the following terms.

take the stump _____

whistle-stop campaign _____

transcontinental railroad line _____

⭐ **3** Match the presidential candidate with the kind of campaigning he used most.

_____ Stephen Douglas   a. campaigning by airplane

_____ William Jennings Bryan   b. front-porch campaigning

_____ William McKinley   c. television campaigning

_____ Herbert Hoover   d. taking the stump on his own behalf

_____ Dwight Eisenhower   e. whistle-stop campaigning

_____ Ronald Reagan   f. radio campaigning

⭐ **4** Name four inventions that changed political campaigns.

_____

_____

* ⭐ **5** Until the late 1800s, most candidates let their supporters come to them, and campaigns cost very little. Today, candidates rely on television. This is a very costly way to campaign, but it reaches many more voters. Would we be better off saving money by going back to front-porch campaigns? Explain your answer.

_____

_____

* ⭐ **6** In what ways do you think computers have changed political campaigns?

_____

_____

* ⭐ **7** Which two nominees participated in the first nationally televised presidential debates?

_____   _____

    reproducible

The Modern Campaign

AFTER HE LOST THE PRESIDENTIAL election to Dwight Eisenhower in 1952, Adlai Stevenson described a typical day of campaigning. Every morning, he said, "you must emerge bright and bubbling with wisdom and well-being." Then you spend a long day shaking thousands of hands, making inspiring speeches, talking on the phone, conferring with political leaders, smiling "until your mouth is dehydrated by the wind," and waving "until the blood runs out of your arm." At the end of the day, Stevenson concluded, "sleep, sweet sleep, steals you away, unless you worry—which I do."

This is how candidates spend every day between Labor Day and election day. They crisscross the country trying to convince voters from Hawaii to Maine that they are more trustworthy and capable than their opponents. They also want to persuade voters that their solutions to the nation's problems are better than their opponents'.

In most elections, candidates have different ideas about how to handle important issues. Some of these are **domestic** issues, which only affect the citizens of our nation. Unemployment, medical aid for the elderly and the poor, and the tax rate are some of the domestic issues candidates have addressed in recent campaigns. Candidates also debate **foreign policy** issues. These include our country's policy on nuclear weapons, treaties with other countries, and the role of our military in other parts of the world.

Candidates hire political advisors to plan a winning campaign **strategy.** Professional speechwriters carefully prepare the words that explain candidates' stands on the issues in a witty and intelligent style. Candidates also employ political **media** experts, who determine how to reach the greatest number of voters through radio, television, and newspapers. Each candidate tries to get as much free publicity as possible through newspaper and magazine interviews, press conferences, and appearances on radio and television talk shows.

Volunteers are the backbone of every campaign. They donate hundreds of hours of their time to help their candidate get elected. Volunteers help operate the campaign headquarters that spring up in every state.

They organize rallies, parades, and fund-raising events when their candidate comes to town. In a process called canvassing, volunteers go door to door passing out information and explaining to people why their candidate should be elected.

The Modern Campaign

Name _____

★1 After candidates are nominated, how many months does a presidential election campaign last?

_____

★2 List three things a candidate does during a presidential election campaign.

_____

_____

_____

★3 Match each word with its definition.

_____ strategy   a. inside the nation

_____ media   b. a careful plan

_____ domestic   c. person who works without pay to help others

_____ volunteer   d. newspapers, radio, and television

★4 What does a candidate hire a political media expert to do?

_____

* ★5 Adlai Stevenson said he often stayed awake worrying after a long, hard day of campaigning. What are some of the things a candidate might worry about?

_____

_____

* ★6 One of Lyndon B. Johnson's campaign slogans was *LBJ for the USA*. Invent a catchy campaign **slogan** using your name.

_____

_____

** ★7 Ask one of your parents or another adult what they think are today's most important:

domestic issues _____

_____

foreign policy issues _____

_____

Financing the Campaign

IN 1860, ABRAHAM LINCOLN SPENT LESS than $700 financing his presidential campaign. In 1996, Bill Clinton raised almost $200 million to run his campaign for reelection. This includes the costs of campaigning for primaries, conventions, and general election. Over the years, campaigns have become longer, more complicated, and more expensive.

In the last century, campaigns were conducted through newspapers and by local supporters talking to their neighbors. Today, presidential campaigns involve as many as 500 paid staff members. Campaign managers, media experts, press secretaries, speech writers, and perhaps even hairdressers, doctors, and fashion experts travel with each candidate. Transportation, hotel, and meal costs for all these people run into millions of dollars. There are also staff salaries and office rents for campaign headquarters around the country. In addition, presidential candidates spend huge sums of money on media advertising.

Candidates must also employ attorneys and accountants. These people keep track of the campaign's **finances** and make sure the campaign committee obeys campaign financing laws. One of the most important people on every candidate's staff today is the finance director. This person is in charge of raising money through mailing requests, dinners, and telephone appeals. To run a successful political campaign, candidates have to work almost as hard raising money as they do winning votes.

In the 1960s, people began to worry that the need to raise so much money would lead to **corruption.** Wealthy **donors** might agree to give money to a candidate only if the candidate would promise to do favors in return. People were also concerned that candidates without a lot of money would never be able to win.

In the 1970s, Congress passed several campaign **reform** laws. These laws made three major changes in campaign financing:

1. The amount of money an individual or a group can give to a candidate is limited. Candidates must keep careful records of all the contributions they receive.

2. The amount of money presidential candidates can spend on their campaigns is limited.

3. Candidates can now receive federal funding to help pay for their campaigns. However, if candidates accept public funding, they must agree to limit money they accept from other sources.

Since the 1970s, **Political Action Committees (PACs)** have played an important role in campaigns. These are organizations set up by **special interest groups** such as lawyers, unions, conservatives, or liberals. They can contribute only a limited amount of money directly to candidates. But they can spend as much as they want on their own independent campaigns to support candidates.

Unfortunately, campaign reform laws have not really stopped the spiraling rise in the cost of running political campaigns. In the winter of 1999, political experts predicted that a candidate would need to raise about $20 million before election year even began just to stay in the race to get nominated by his or her party.

Name _____

★1 About $193,400,000 was spent in 1988 on presidential campaigns in the United States. Write this figure out in words.

_____

In 1988, there were about 178,000,000 people over the age of 18 in the United States. How much was spent in the 1988 campaign for each person?

_____

★2 Use the context of the section or a dictionary to define the following words.

finances _____

corruption _____

donors _____

reform _____

★3 Political experts think that candidates would need _____ before election year even begins to get nominated by his or her party.

a. $2 billion   b. $10 million   c. $20 million   d. $275 million

★4 Name four employees that may serve on a campaign staff today.

_____

_____

★5 Political candidates often seek the endorsements of movie stars and professional athletes. Why do you think support from famous people is considered important in today's campaigns?

_____

_____

* ★6 In your opinion, are candidates helped or hurt by the law limiting how much they can spend on a campaign? Explain your answer.

_____

_____

* ★7 Why do you think doctors, teachers, or business people might be interested in donating money to someone's campaign?

_____

_____

* ★8 Why are people concerned that large donations from single individuals or powerful organizations will lead to political corruption?

_____

Public Opinion Polls

IN 1824, REPORTERS FOR A PENNSYLVANIA newspaper stood on street corners in Delaware and asked passers-by who they planned to vote for in the next election. The results of their interviews were compiled and published. This was the first formal political opinion **poll** taken in the United States. This was the first time the public had been surveyed to find out who might be president before the election.

As time went on, polls became much larger. In 1916, the magazine *Literary Digest* began to mail mock ballots to voters all over the country. Voters were asked to state their preference for president. In four straight elections, the magazine's polls accurately predicted the winning candidate. But then, in 1936, after polling two million voters, *Literary Digest* confidently predicted that Governor Alf Landon of Kansas would defeat President Franklin Roosevelt. The magazine was dead wrong. Roosevelt won the election by more than 11 million votes.

During the next 12 years, political polling became more scientific. Pollsters tried to ask their questions of a cross section of the country. Rich and poor, men and women, the old and the young were asked for whom they planned to vote.

But the 1948 election demonstrated that this new, more scientific polling was still not perfect. Almost all the pollsters predicted that Republican Thomas E. Dewey would defeat President Harry Truman. One newspaper even printed the headline *Dewey Defeats Truman* after only a few votes were counted. The next morning, President Truman gleefully waved a copy of the newspaper for reporters as he celebrated his victory over Dewey.

Polls have correctly predicted the results of every presidential election since 1952, except for the 1968 and 1976 elections, which were too close to call. Polls are not only interesting to voters, but are also useful to the candidates. As soon as people announce their candidacy, polls start measuring who is most popular. People even use polls to help them decide if they should run in the first place. A good showing in the polls can also help a candidate raise money to continue campaigning.

Candidates often use polls to help plan campaign strategies. They are especially interested in "undecided" voters. Candidates will frequently have polls done just for them so they can find out what kinds of people these undecided voters are. Then the candidates will tailor their campaigns according to poll results.

Although polls have become more accurate, many Americans are concerned that they unfairly influence the outcome of elections. Candidates who are ahead in the polls have an easier time raising money, which in turn, helps put them even farther ahead. Supporters of candidates who are behind sometimes switch their votes to a "winner" or just don't bother to vote. Despite these concerns, polling voters before elections will probably remain a permanent part of the election process.

Name _____

⭐**1** What is an opinion poll?

_____

⭐**2** Why is it important for a poll to reflect the opinions of a cross section of people?

_____

⭐**3** Opinion polls are used for which of the following? (Circle the correct answer.)

   a. to help candidates raise money

   b. to tell who is ahead in an election race

   c. to help people decide whether to run for office

   d. to identify undecided voters

   e. *b* and *c*

   f. all of the above

⭐**4** In 1936, the country was in the middle of the Great Depression. Many people lost their jobs, homes, and cars, and had no telephone. The *Literary Digest* used phone books and lists of car owners to get names for its election poll. Why was this probably the reason their poll results were wrong?

_____

_____

*⭐**5** The *Literary Digest* went out of business after the 1936 presidential election. Why do you think this happened?

_____

_____

*⭐**6** Thomas Dewey felt that being so far ahead in the polls helped cause his defeat. Why do you think he felt this way?

_____

_____

⭐7** Bring in the results of a recent public opinion poll from a newspaper or magazine. Share the article with your class, and discuss the results. Did someone pay to have this poll taken? Do you think the results are accurate for a cross section of the nation?

⭐8** Have the class divide into groups to conduct personal preference polls at school or in the community. Have each group write a short paragraph explaining what they plan to poll and how they will select samplings to get an accurate cross section of opinions about the chosen issue. Have groups share their results.

Campaigning by Television

THE FIRST YEAR TELEVISION MADE A difference in a presidential campaign was 1960. At the beginning of the campaign, John F. Kennedy was the **underdog.** This 43-year-old senator from Massachusetts faced an uphill battle against Richard Nixon. Nixon was familiar to voters across the country because he had served as vice president during Dwight Eisenhower's two terms of office. But Kennedy was witty and handsome and able to use television to his advantage.

The candidates agreed to four televised debates. On September 26, 1960, 70 million people watched the first televised presidential campaign debate in the country's history. Both men were well-prepared, but while Kennedy seemed relaxed and self-assured, Nixon looked pale, nervous, and tired. People who listened to the debate on the radio thought Nixon did as well as, if not better, than Kennedy. Most of those who saw the debate on television, even Nixon supporters, declared Kennedy the winner. For the next three debates, Nixon gained weight and used makeup to improve his appearance. But fewer people watched those debates.

The vote in November 1960 was very close. Kennedy received only .2% more votes than Nixon. Most historians agree that the voters Kennedy won over on the television debates made the difference in this remarkably close election.

No television debate since 1960 has been watched by as many people, and none has made such a difference in the outcome of an election. But today, television is essential to presidential campaigns.

Television is the best way to reach the largest number of voters. An ad during a particularly popular television program may reach 50 million people or more. A story on the nightly television news will probably be seen by about 20 million people. A newspaper ad or article would have to appear in at least 20 of the biggest daily newspapers to reach that many people.

A large part of each candidate's campaign budget is now spent on television commercials. During the last two weeks before the 1984 election, Ronald Reagan and Walter Mondale spent $8 million on national television

commercials and $7 million more on local television ads in key areas of the country. Each candidate spent $130,000 to buy a 30-second ad on the Monday night football game before election day.

Because television commercials are so expensive, candidates try to get as much free exposure as they can. Candidates invite network reporters to travel with them to cover the campaign. An incumbent president running for reelection has an advantage, because most of what the president does on the job every day is newsworthy.

Television has allowed more people than ever before to see and hear the candidates. But its effect on campaigns has also been criticized. On television, a story must usually be told in 30 to 60 seconds, and it must be interesting to view. Many people feel that television makes candidates' **images** more important than their experience, ability, or stands on issues.

Campaigning by Television

Name _____

★1 Use the context of the section or a dictionary to define the following words.

underdog _____

image _____

★2 On the first nationally televised debate between presidential candidates, which candidate had the better image?

_____

Why were people who heard the debate on the radio more impressed with Nixon's performance than those who saw him on television?

_____

_____

★3 How has television improved our presidential campaigns?

_____

_____

What disadvantages has it brought to the election process?

_____

_____

★4 The purpose of TV campaign commercials is to reach as many voters as possible. During which of the following shows are you *least* likely to see a political ad? (Circle the correct answer.)

    a. a football game   c. a TV movie

    b. a soap opera   d. Saturday morning cartoons

* ★5 Do you think political campaign ads are helpful to candidates who are not well known to the public? Explain your answer.

_____

_____

* ★6 Do you think people are likely to change their minds about who to vote for after seeing TV ads? Explain your answer.

_____

_____

** ★7 Interview two adults and ask them if television coverage of the candidates helps them decide for whom to vote. Summarize your interviews on a separate sheet of paper.

Other Campaign Media

TELEVISION MAY BE THE BEST WAY TO reach the largest number of voters at once, but other media provide information about candidates, too. For example, newspaper and magazine articles provide more thorough coverage of candidates' backgrounds and views.

Early in the country's history, newspapers freely mixed fact and opinion. If a newspaper strongly supported one candidate, it didn't hesitate to **slant** articles in favor of that person and **slander** his opponents. Today, opinions about candidates are printed on the **editorial** page, where readers know they are reading personal viewpoints. A variety of viewpoints are presented, but a few weeks before the election, most newspapers make **endorsements.** The editorial board explains why it thinks one candidate is better qualified than the others.

During the 19th century, **political cartoons** played an important role in presidential elections. The most famous political cartoonist, Thomas Nast, was called the "Maker of Presidents," because his cartoons so effectively made fun of or pointed out the weaknesses of candidates he did not support. Today, political cartoonists continue to mold opinion by using pictures to show candidates' weaknesses.

In the 1930s and 1940s, radio was the most important channel of communication between politicians and the public. Today, candidates still make use of paid radio advertisements and interview programs to reach voters. They not only produce radio and TV ads, but also handbills, letters to voters, posters, buttons, bumper stickers, and even billboards. These campaign materials reflect the image candidates want voters to believe.

There are a number of advertising **techniques** that candidates use in ads and printed materials to persuade voters to support them. The next time there is a campaign, see if you can spot some of these techniques.

1. **Endorsements.** Many athletes and actors are better known than most politicians. Candidates usually seek the endorsements of celebrities. They hope that voters will be influenced by the support of famous people.

2. **The Bandwagon.** Advertisers know that people like to do the same things their friends and neighbors are doing. If people think that everybody else is buying a product or voting for a candidate, they will be tempted to "jump on the bandwagon." This is the thinking in ads that tell us "More people use Brand X."

3. **Name Calling.** In close races, candidates are more likely to resort to this technique. They may accuse their opponents of being "irresponsible" or "favoring special interests."

4. **Glittering Generalities.** This method uses **slogans** or phrases with which no one could disagree, but are too general to have any real meaning. If a candidate says, "I'm for peace," or "I'm the education candidate," no one can disapprove. But such generalities tell us little about what the candidate really believes.

5. **Plain-Folks Appeal.** Candidates want to persuade voters that they understand their everyday problems. Campaign materials may show photographs of candidates playing with their children or sharing lunch with workers at a construction site.

Name _____

⭐1 What are three sources of information about political candidates?

_____

_____

_____

⭐2 Use the context of the section or a dictionary to define the following words.

editorial _____

slander _____

endorsements _____

slogan _____

⭐3 What kind of media provide the most detailed coverage of candidates' experience and ideas?

_____

⭐4 On what page do most newspapers carry opinion articles?

_____

⭐5 Buttons that said "I like Ike" were distributed during Dwight Eisenhower's presidential campaign. Of which advertising technique is this an example?

_____

⭐6 One of Richard Nixon's campaign slogans was "Forward Together." Of which advertising technique is this an example?

_____

* ⭐7 Think of a favorite singer, actor, or athlete. Would that person's endorsement make you want to support a candidate? Explain your answer.

_____

_____

* ⭐8 If a radio or television station presents an editorial opinion, it must obey the "fairness doctrine." This means that the station must provide free air time for opposing points of view. Explain whether you think this is a good law.

_____

_____

** ⭐9 Find an example of one of Nast's political cartoons, and answer the following questions: *What presidents did Thomas Nast help elect? How did he influence voters?*

reproducible

Election Day

ON THE FIRST TUESDAY AFTER THE first Monday in November of an election year, the long campaign for the presidency is over. There is nothing more the candidates can do. They return to their hometowns, where, like millions of other Americans, they will go to their neighborhood polling places to vote.

Many different kinds of buildings serve as polling places. Polling booths are set up in schools, churches, town halls, firehouses, and even private garages. Several election officials are assigned to work at each polling place. These people check voter names on registration lists to make sure that each person who comes in is eligible to vote in that **precinct.** They also make sure each person votes only once.

Once voters receive their ballots, they step into an enclosed booth, draw the curtain, and mark their ballots. Many precincts use voting machines. The voter pushes levers by the names of candidates. Then the voter pulls a handle, and the machine records the votes and resets the levers for the next voter. Some precincts use paper ballots. The voter marks his or her choices and hands the ballot to an election officer. Paper ballots may be counted by hand, as all ballots once were. But today, they are more likely to be punch cards that can be counted by a machine.

The right to vote privately is an important part of the election process. But we have had this right for only the last 100 years or so. Before 1888, voters had to call out their chosen candidates to election clerks. Because voting was public, people could bully voters into voting for certain candidates. Sometimes voters would "sell" their votes by agreeing to vote a certain way in exchange for money.

The adoption of the secret ballot ended much of this corruption. Voting became private when all candidates' names were listed on the same ballot and voting was done in a closed booth. This was sometimes called the **"Australian ballot"** because Australians had been voting in private since 1858. The secret ballot was first used in a local election in Louisville, Kentucky in 1888. It soon spread to all the states, except South Carolina, which held out until 1950.

No one can campaign in polling places, but many volunteers work all day in a final effort to get their candidate selected. Many serve as **poll watchers.** They help to see that the election is run fairly. Volunteers also drive voters to the polls, telephone party members to remind them to vote, and baby-sit so parents can get to the polls.

Once a candidate has the 270 electoral college votes needed to win the election, the losing candidate usually makes a **concession statement.** In this speech at campaign headquarters, the runner-up thanks supporters and congratulates the winner. The television cameras then switch to the headquarters of the victorious candidate. The winner makes a victory statement to voters across the nation as well as campaign staff and volunteers who have gathered to celebrate many months of hard work.

After losing the 1952 election, Adlai Stevenson said he was reminded of a story Abraham Lincoln used to tell. "They asked him how he felt once after an unsuccessful election. He said he felt like a boy who had stubbed his toe in the dark. He said that he was too old to cry, but it hurt too much to laugh."

© Good Apple GA13053

Name _____

⭐**1** Why is it important for people to vote in secrecy?

_____

_____

⭐**2** How does the Australian ballot allow people to keep their votes secret?

_____

_____

_____

⭐**3** Place a checkmark next to the ways that volunteers help candidates on election day.

_____ drive voters to the polls

_____ call people to remind them to vote

_____ put up campaign posters in polling places

_____ take care of children so parents can vote

_____ hand out campaign buttons in front of polling places

⭐**4** What are poll watchers?

_____

⭐**5** What are concession statements?

_____

* ⭐**6** Why do you think campaigning is forbidden at polling places on election day?

_____

_____

* ⭐**7** Election results would be counted sooner if polling places closed at 5 p.m. or 6 p.m. Why do you think polls are open until 8 p.m. or 9 p.m.?

_____

_____

** ⭐**8** Use a dictionary or encyclopedia to find the origin of the word *ballot*.

_____

_____

_____

reproducible

Notable Elections

THE LONGEST AND MOST DISPUTED presidential election in the nation's history was the election of 1876. The Republican candidate was Rutherford B. Hayes, the governor of Ohio. The Democratic candidate was Samuel J. Tilden, New York's governor. Both were honest, able men. They agreed on many important issues, but their campaigns were soon marked by **mudslinging.** Each man accused the other of being a crook.

On election night, it looked like Tilden had won. He had 260,000 more popular votes than Hayes, and he had 184 electoral votes to Hayes's 165. But 20 electoral votes from four states were in doubt. Tilden needed only one more to get the 185 votes needed, at that time, to win the election. Hayes went to bed on election night thinking he had lost.

But the dispute over those 20 votes lasted almost four months. Nineteen of the votes in question came from southern states where the voting had been marked by fraud, bribery, and violence. Finally, Congress appointed an electoral commission to decide the matter. The group originally consisted of seven Democrats, seven Republicans, and one independent. But at the last minute, the independent had to resign. A Republican judge took his place. By a vote of eight to seven, the commission gave all the disputed votes to Hayes, the Republican candidate. Two days before the inauguration, the country learned that Hayes, by a margin of one electoral vote, was to be the next president of the United States.

While the election of 1912 was not very close, like that of 1876, it was one of the most lively and interesting. Republican Theodore Roosevelt had served two terms as president, from 1901 to 1908. In 1904, he declared that he would not run for a third term. By the end of Republican President Taft's term in 1912, Roosevelt changed his mind. An enormously popular candidate, Roosevelt won nine state primaries. Taft won only one. But at the Republican convention, Taft's supporters were able to renominate Taft.

In response, Roosevelt decided to run as a third-party candidate under the Progressive party banner.

Meanwhile, the Democrats had nominated Woodrow Wilson, governor of New Jersey. Roosevelt and Taft spent more time calling each other names than campaigning against Wilson. Roosevelt, it is rumored, even insisted on making a speech after he had been shot in the chest. Despite Roosevelt's lively campaign style, the calm, intelligent Wilson was able to convince voters that he was the best choice. He won a landslide victory with 435 electoral votes to Roosevelt's 88 and Taft's 8.

Name _____

★1 When Rutherford B. Hayes was president, many newspapers called him "Old 8 to 7" or "His Fraudulency." Why do you suppose this honest man was called these names?

_____

_____

★2 How was the 1876 presidential election finally decided?

_____

_____

_____

★3 Why does the election of 1912 stand out in the history of presidential elections?

_____

_____

★4 Define the word *mudslinging*. Then give an example.

_____

_____

★5 Write W (Wilson), R (Roosevelt), or T (Taft) to fill in the blanks below.

_____ a. elected president in 1908   _____ d. won the 1912 election

_____ b. formed a third party   _____ e. won only one state primary

_____ c. did little campaigning   _____ f. president from 1901 to 1908

** ★6 What was the nickname for Teddy Roosevelt's Progressive party?

_____

** ★7 Poll ten adults about the most memorable presidential election they remember. Compile class findings on a graph.

** ★8 Many elections in United States history have proved to be interesting, exciting, and even unusual. Those in 1860, 1924, 1928, 1932, 1948, and 1960 were especially interesting. Find out what happened during one of these elections that made it so extraordinary.

Inauguration Day

FINALLY, WE HAVE ARRIVED AT Inauguration Day, the culmination of the election process. Until 1933, Inauguration Day was March 4. Then the 20th Amendment was passed, which made January 20 the day the new president and vice president are sworn into office. This amendment shortens the time that **"lame ducks"** remain in office after their replacements are elected.

Although the date changed, new presidents still take the same oath of office as George Washington. They promise to carry out the office of the president and to "preserve, protect, and defend the Constitution of the United States." Thousands of visitors flock to Washington, D.C., each Inauguration Day to hear the president take the oath of office and deliver the inaugural address, the new president's first speech.

Throughout the nation's history, presidents have used this speech to talk about their goals for the next four years. If the election was an especially bitter contest, they will often call for unity. In 1800, when Thomas Jefferson became president, political parties were a new development. Some people feared that Jefferson would listen only to members of his own party and ignore those of the losing party. But he calmed their fears by calling for "harmony and affection." He told his audience that "every difference of opinion is not a difference of principle."

In 1865, our nation was in the midst of a civil war. President Abraham Lincoln's call for unity is perhaps the most famous inaugural address. "With malice toward none," he said, "with charity for all . . . let us strive on to finish the work we are in; to bind up the nation's wounds . . . to do all which may achieve and cherish a just and lasting peace among ourselves, and with all nations."

Another famous inaugural speech was that of President Franklin Roosevelt in 1933. Then, our country was in the midst of the Great Depression. Roosevelt told the nation there was hope—things would get better. "The only thing we have to fear," he claimed, "is fear itself."

In 1961, President John F. Kennedy gave a stirring inaugural address, in which he said, "My fellow

Americans, ask not what your country can do for you, but what you can do for your country."

The Constitution does not require the president to give an inaugural address, but it has become a tradition. The inaugural parade and the inaugural ball have become traditions as well. Both have become more colorful and elaborate over the years. In 1809, James Madison's wife, Dolly, hosted the first inaugural ball for 400 people. Since then, it has become a popular way to reward important supporters of the new president. Today, there are usually four or five inaugural balls going on in Washington the night after the president is sworn into office.

Name _____

★1 On what day of the year is Inauguration Day? _____

★2 A president whose successor has been elected is a _____ president.

★3 Which event on Inauguration Day is not described in the Constitution?

_____

★4 Which amendment set Inauguration Day as January 20?

_____

★5 Match the president and the phrase from his inaugural address.

_____ Thomas Jefferson   a. "Ask not what your country can do for you, but what you can do for your country."

_____ Abraham Lincoln   b. "The only thing we have to fear is fear itself."

_____ Franklin Roosevelt   c. "Every difference of opinion is not a difference of principle."

_____ John F. Kennedy   d. "With malice toward none, with charity for all . . ."

** ★6 Why did supporters of the 20th Amendment wish to shorten the "lame duck" period?

_____

_____

** ★7 Find out why Inauguration Day was originally set for four months after election day. What changes in our society allowed it to be moved to an earlier date?

_____

_____

** ★8 Presidents usually take the oath of office on the steps of the Capitol Building in Washington, D.C. However, there have been some exceptions. Where did Lyndon B. Johnson take the oath of office?

_____

_____

reproducible

Should We Change the System?

ONE OF THE GREAT STRENGTHS OF OUR Constitution and the government it created is the ability to change when necessary. This flexibility has allowed our election process to become much more fair over the years. Many people agree that further changes could make our system even better.

Many voters believe that our presidents should be elected directly by the people. They think a constitutional amendment should be passed to end the electoral college. Many efforts have been made to eliminate the electoral college, but none have yet succeeded.

Another change many people would like is stricter rules about campaign spending. In recent years, laws have been passed that set limits on campaign spending. Now people are concerned about the Political Action Committees. Because these groups campaign independently, they are not restricted by the current laws.

Another frequent complaint is that our presidential campaigns are too long. Many people believe the long campaigns create exhausted candidates, overly expensive campaigns, and bored voters. All primaries could be held on the same day instead of being spaced over five months. Or we could follow England's example and have a one-month campaign period. Opponents of a shorter campaign period believe, however, that voters would not have enough time to thoroughly evaluate the candidates.

Many people would also like to change the role of television in campaigns. One of the most serious complaints is about the television networks' practice of announcing the winner before polls have closed everywhere around the country. By polling people who have just voted, the networks project the election results long before all ballots are counted. In 1980, the networks predicted Reagan's landslide victory over President Carter early in the evening. Carter made his concession speech an hour before the polls closed on the West Coast. Democrats claimed that many people in the West did not even bother to vote once Reagan's victory was announced.

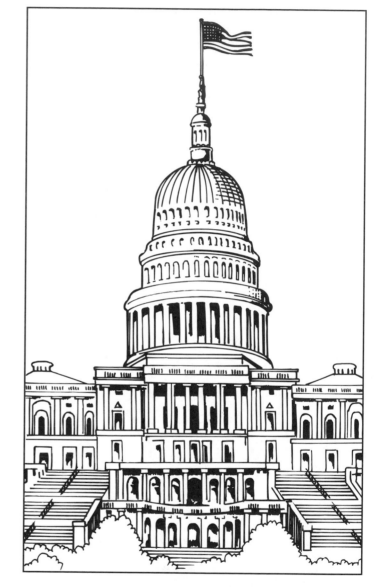

Finally, low voter turnout is a matter of concern. In 1996, only 49% of eligible voters voted in the presidential campaign. Some people think that voting should be required of all eligible citizens. Others think that the United States should follow Australia's example and fine anyone who fails to vote.

As you have read, the way we elect our presidents has changed over the generations. How will it change in your lifetime?

Should We Change the System?

Name _____

⭐1 Which is not a way that our presidential election system has changed since 1787?

    a. The electorate expanded to include almost every U.S. citizen over 18.

    b. U.S. citizens now vote directly for the president.

    c. More ordinary citizens now have a say in who will be nominated as the parties' presidential candidates.

    d. Each party now chooses its own nominees for president and vice president.

⭐2 Mark the following statements true (T) or false (F).

    _____ England's campaign periods are longer than ours.

    _____ Australians can be fined if they don't vote.

    _____ Television networks often announce winners before all ballots are counted.

    _____ There are no limits on campaign spending.

*⭐3 Place a checkmark by the changes you would like to see in the way we elect presidents.

    _____ Eliminate the electoral college.

    _____ Limit campaign spending by Political Action Committees.

    _____ Shorten the period of presidential campaigns.

    _____ Require the media to wait until all the polls are closed before announcing a winner.

    _____ Require all eligible voters to vote in every election.

*⭐4 Is there anything else you would change about the way we elect our presidents? If so, what would you change, and why?

_____

_____

_____

*⭐5 Why do you think so few Americans exercise their right to vote?

_____

_____

**⭐6 Write to the manager of a local network TV station. Ask what the network policy is for announcing the winner of a presidential election. Will the network wait until the polls have closed all across the country? (You might have your class divide into groups to do this research, each writing to a different network.)

51

reproducible

The Presidents of the United States

1. George Washington
In office: 1789–1797
Elected from Virginia
No party affiliation
Previous jobs: surveyor, plantation owner, military officer, state legislator

2. John Adams
In office: 1797–1801
Elected from Massachusetts
Federalist
Previous jobs: lawyer, diplomat, vice president

3. Thomas Jefferson
In office: 1801–1809
Elected from Virginia
Democratic-Republican
Previous jobs: lawyer, plantation owner, state legislator, governor of Virginia, diplomat, secretary of state, vice president

4. James Madison
In office: 1809–1817
Elected from Virginia
Democratic-Republican
Previous jobs: lawyer, writer, state legislator, representative, secretary of state

5. James Monroe
In office: 1817–1825
Elected from Virginia
Democratic-Republican
Previous jobs: lawyer, state legislator, senator, diplomat, governor of Virginia, secretary of state, secretary of war

6. John Quincy Adams
In office: 1825–1829
Elected from Massachusetts
National-Republican
Previous jobs: lawyer, professor, senator, diplomat, secretary of state

7. Andrew Jackson
In office: 1829–1837
Elected from Tennessee
Democrat
Previous jobs: saddler, racing stable owner, military officer, lawyer, representative, judge, senator

8. Martin Van Buren
In office: 1837–1841
Elected from New York
Democrat
Previous jobs: lawyer, state legislator, state attorney general, senator, governor of New York, secretary of state, vice president

9. William Henry Harrison
In office: 1841
Elected from Ohio
Whig
Previous jobs: military officer, governor of Indiana Territory, representative, senator

10. John Tyler
In office: 1841–1845
Elected from Virginia
Whig
Previous jobs: lawyer, representative, governor of Virginia, senator, vice president

11. James K. Polk
In office: 1845–1849
Elected from Tennessee
Democrat
Previous jobs: lawyer, state legislator, representative, governor of Tennessee

12. Zachary Taylor
In office: 1849–1850
Elected from Louisiana
Whig
Previous jobs: plantation owner, military officer

13. Millard Fillmore
In office: 1850–1853
Elected from New York
Whig
Previous jobs: wool carder, teacher, lawyer, state legislator, representative, comptroller of New York, vice president

14. Franklin Pierce
In office: 1853–1857
Elected from New Hampshire
Democrat
Previous jobs: lawyer, state legislator, representative, senator

15. James Buchanan
In office: 1857–1861
Elected from Pennsylvania
Democrat
Previous jobs: lawyer, representative, senator, secretary of state, diplomat

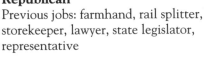

16. Abraham Lincoln
In office: 1861–1865
Elected from Illinois
Republican
Previous jobs: farmhand, rail splitter, storekeeper, lawyer, state legislator, representative

17. Andrew Johnson
In office: 1865–1869
Elected from Tennessee
Democrat
Previous jobs: tailor, mayor, state legislator, representative, governor of Tennessee, senator, vice president

18. Ulysses S. Grant
In office: 1869–1877
Elected from Illinois
Republican
Previous jobs: military officer, farmer, real estate salesman

19. Rutherford B. Hayes
In office: 1877–1881
Elected from Ohio
Republican
Previous jobs: lawyer, representative, governor of Ohio

20. James A. Garfield
In office: 1881
Elected from Ohio
Republican
Previous jobs: canal driver, professor, college president, lawyer, lay preacher, state legislator, representative

21. Chester A. Arthur
In office: 1881–1885
Elected from New York
Republican
Previous jobs: lawyer, civil servant, vice president

22. Grover Cleveland
In office: 1885–1889
Elected from New York
Democrat
Previous jobs: lawyer, mayor, governor of New York

23. Benjamin Harrison
In office: 1889–1893
Elected from Indiana
Republican
Previous jobs: lawyer, senator

24. Grover Cleveland
In office: 1893–1897
Elected from New York
Democrat
Previous jobs: lawyer, mayor, governor of New York

25. William McKinley
In office: 1897–1901
Elected from Ohio
Republican
Previous jobs: teacher, lawyer, representative, governor of Ohio

26. Theodore Roosevelt
In office: 1901–1909
Elected from New York
Republican
Previous jobs: author, state legislator, rancher, head of New York City police board, assistant secretary of the Navy, military officer, vice president

27. William H. Taft
In office: 1909–1913
Elected from Ohio
Republican
Previous jobs: lawyer, judge, civil governor of the Philippines, secretary of war

28. Woodrow Wilson
In office: 1913–1921
Elected from New Jersey
Democrat
Previous jobs: lawyer, professor, college president, governor of New Jersey

29. Warren G. Harding
In office: 1921–1923
Elected from Ohio
Republican
Previous jobs: newspaper publisher, state legislator, lieutenant governor of Ohio, senator

30. Calvin Coolidge
In office: 1923–1929
Elected from Massachusetts
Republican
Previous jobs: lawyer, state legislator, governor of Massachusetts, vice president

31. Herbert C. Hoover
In office: 1929–1933
Elected from California
Republican
Previous jobs: miner, mining engineer, secretary of commerce

32. Franklin D. Roosevelt
In office: 1933–1945
Elected from New York
Democrat
Previous jobs: state legislator, assistant secretary of the Navy, governor of New York

33. Harry S Truman
In office: 1945–1953
Elected from Missouri
Democrat
Previous jobs: bank clerk, farmer, county administrator, haberdasher, senator, vice president

34. Dwight D. Eisenhower
In office: 1953–1961
Elected from Pennsylvania
Republican
Previous jobs: military officer, university president, NATO commander

35. John F. Kennedy
In office: 1961–1963
Elected from Massachusetts
Democrat
Previous jobs: representative, senator

36. Lyndon B. Johnson
In office: 1963–1969
Elected from Texas
Democrat
Previous jobs: rancher, teacher, representative, senator, vice president

37. Richard M. Nixon
In office: 1969–1974
Elected from New York
Republican
Previous jobs: lawyer, representative, senator, vice president

38. Gerald R. Ford
In office: 1974–1977
Elected from Michigan
Republican
Previous jobs: lawyer, representative, vice president

39. Jimmy Carter
In office: 1977–1981
Elected from Georgia
Democrat
Previous jobs: peanut farmer, state legislator, governor of Georgia

40. Ronald W. Reagan
In office: 1981–1989
Elected from California
Republican
Previous jobs: movie actor, governor of California

41. George H. W. Bush
In office: 1989–1993
Elected from Texas
Republican
Previous jobs: oilman, representative, U.S. ambassador to the U.N., director of the C.I.A., vice president

42. William J. Clinton
In office: 1993–present
Elected from Arkansas
Democrat
Previous jobs: college instructor, state attorney general, governor of Arkansas

The Presidents of the United States

Name _____

⭐**1** From which state or states were the largest number of presidents elected?

_____

_____

Have any presidents been elected from your state? If so, who are they?

_____

_____

⭐**2** Which president served the longest? _____

For how many terms was he elected? _____

⭐**3** Which president or presidents served only one year or less?

_____

What happened to him (or them)?

_____

⭐**4** Since 1856, when the Republicans first nominated a presidential candidate, how many presidential elections have the Republicans won? _____ Since Andrew Jackson first won in 1828, how many presidential elections have the Democrats won? _____

⭐**5** Who was the only president to serve two nonconsecutive terms?

_____

⭐**6** How many presidents were lawyers? _____ How many presidents served in Congress as representatives or senators? _____ How many were state legislators? _____ How many were state governors? _____ How many were vice presidents? _____

⭐**7** Which presidents never held an elected public office before they became president?

_____

_____

** ⭐**8** Which president was never actually elected president or vice president?

_____

** ⭐**9** Which presidents lost when they ran for a second (or third) term?

_____

_____

Glossary

Australian Ballot ballot that has all the names of all the people running for public office. It is given to the voter at the voting place to be marked in secret.

Ballot piece of paper or other object used in voting.

Cabinet the heads of the departments of the executive branch of the federal government; they advise the president.

Candidate person who seeks, or is nominated for, an office; a nominee.

Caucus meeting of members or leaders of a political party to make plans, choose candidates, or decide how to vote.

Closed Primary election in which Democrats are only allowed to vote for Democrats, and Republicans are only allowed to vote for Republicans.

Committed Delegate a delegate who promises to vote for a certain candidate.

Compromise to settle a quarrel or difference of opinion by agreeing that each will give up a part of what he or she is demanding.

Concession Statement speech made by a candidate that formally announces that he or she has lost an election.

Congress the lawmaking branch of the United States government; includes the Senate and the House of Representatives.

Convention a meeting of delegates from a political party.

Corruption dishonesty; the use of unlawful means to tempt someone to do wrong.

Crossover Vote vote by a member of one party for a candidate of another party.

Dark Horse an unexpected candidate about whom little is known; a person unexpectedly nominated for political office.

Deadlock a tie that cannot be broken.

Debate (*noun*) formal discussion between two or more people with different points of view about one or more issues; (*verb*) to formally discuss positions on issues.

Delegate person given power or authority to act on behalf of others; a representative.

Democratic of a form of government run either directly by the people or by their elected representatives.

Direct Election election in which voters vote directly for candidates.

Disenfranchise to deprive someone of his or her right to vote.

Domestic inside a nation; not foreign.

Donors people who give money to campaigns or causes.

Editorial (*adjective*) expressing the opinion of a newspaper or its editor.

Electoral College group of people chosen by voters in each state to elect the president and vice president of the United States.

Electorate the people who have the right to vote.

Endorsement statement of approval or support.

Executive Branch the part of the government that has the duty and power to put laws into effect.

Finances money matters; system by which money is raised and managed.

Foreign Policy plan of action regarding other countries.

Front-runner candidate with the best chance of being elected.

House of Representatives lower house of Congress, in which states are represented according to their population.

Image appearance; impression that a person, group, or organization presents to the public.

Inaugurate to swear in office with a ceremony.

Incumbent someone who holds a public office and is running for reelection.

Independent not a member of a political party.

Indirect Election election in which voters elect representatives to vote for candidates.

Judiciary Branch the part of the government that interprets laws and administers justice through a system of courts.

Keynote Speaker person who gives the opening speech at a meeting.

Lame Duck elected official who continues to hold office between the election and the inauguration of the successor.

Landslide an overwhelming majority of votes for one candidate or political party in an election.

Legislative Branch the part of the government that has the duty and power to make laws.

Media radio, television, newspapers, magazines, and other means of mass communication.

Mudslinging attempt to discredit a competitor by not talking about legitimate issues; calling an opponent names.

Nominee person selected to run for public office; a candidate.

Open Primary election in which voters decide on election day whether to vote on a Democratic or Republican ballot.

Over the Top during the counting of votes, the point at which a candidate has won the minimum number of votes necessary to win an election.

Party Boss city or state leader of a political party organization.

Plank part of a political party's platform about a specific issue.

Platform a plan of action or statement of a national party's goals and views on important domestic and foreign policy issues.

Political Action Committee (PAC) independent fund-raising campaign organization set up by a special interest group.

Political Cartoon illustration that shows a viewpoint on a particular issue, usually through symbolism, humor, and satire.

Political Party organization of citizens who have similar views on public issues and work for the election of party members to public office.

Poll (opinion) survey of what the public thinks about a particular subject or candidate.

Poll (voting) place where votes are cast and counted.

Poll Tax special tax, now illegal, that people in some states had to pay before they could vote.

Poll Watcher person who makes sure the election is run fairly.

Precinct local voting district in a county or city.

Primary election in which members of a political party choose candidates to run for office in the general election.

Rank and File common people.

Ratify approve; confirm.

Reform change intended to improve conditions; improvement.

Registered having one's name on a list or record of eligible voters.

Representative member of the United States House of Representatives.

Seconding Speech speech giving additional support after the nomination of a candidate.

Senate upper house of Congress, in which each state is represented by two senators.

Senator member of the United States Senate.

Slander to say untrue things about or misrepresent someone, which results in damaging his or her reputation.

Slant to purposely interpret or present information in a way that supports a special interest or issue.

Slate list of candidates or officers to be considered for appointment, nomination, or election.

Slogan word or phrase used by a business, club, or political party to advertise its purpose; motto.

Special Interest Group group of people who want similar things from the government and work to gain support for their interests.

Strategy plan to accomplish a goal.

Suffrage the right to vote.

Suffragist person who favors giving the right to vote to more people, especially women.

Take the Stump go out and make campaign speeches.

Technique special method or system used to accomplish a goal.

Third Party political organization other than the Democratic and Republican parties, usually set up to work for a special cause.

Tradition beliefs, opinions, or customs handed down from one generation to the next.

Transcontinental Railroad Line railroad line that goes from one end of the country to the other.

Uncommitted Delegate delegate who is able to vote for any candidate.

Underdog candidate or contestant considered unlikely to win.

Volunteer person who offers services to a candidate or organization for free.

Whistle-Stop Campaign early method of campaigning in which a candidate crossed the country by train and made speeches at each place the train stopped.

Winner-Take-All Election election in which the state that receives the most popular votes wins all the state's electoral votes.

Suggested Activities and Projects

★ To help students remember the sequence of events leading to the election of United States presidents, have them make a chart or time line showing the steps in a successful presidential campaign.

★ Have your class organize a schoolwide convention to nominate a school president or mascot. Assign electoral votes by class size, have students make nominating and seconding speeches, and encourage students to plan enthusiastic demonstrations.

★ Bring in several books (see bibliography) that show old campaign posters, slogans, and buttons. Encourage students to browse through these materials, then have each student "run" for president by designing a poster, creating a slogan, and presenting a campaign speech. Or, student pairs can run campaigns for each other.

★ Have each student take a poll about a political candidate or political issue. Then have students illustrate their findings with large graphs that can be displayed around the classroom.

★ Invite someone who has served in an elective public office to speak to your class. Prepare students to ask questions. Students can also write letters to politicians (the president, state governor, local congressperson, senator, and so on). Student questions might include: *Why did you want to run for public office? Do you ever get tired of campaigning? What do you think is our country's biggest problem? Do you think our election process should be changed in any way? How?*

★ Have each student interview a senior citizen about which president he or she most admired, and why. Or students can ask about a memorable presidential election. Invite them to present their findings in written or oral reports.

★ Invite students to bring in political cartoons from magazines and newspapers for a special bulletin board display. Discuss with the class what each cartoonist is trying to say. Encourage students to create their own political cartoons.

★ Ask each student to write an essay titled *If I Were President*.

★ Discuss Political Action Committees (PACs) with students. Talk about why special interest groups, such as doctors, teachers, or gun owners, donate money to candidates they think will support their causes. Ask students whether these groups should be allowed to donate money to political candidates, and which particular interest groups students might support, and why.

★ If you are teaching this unit during an election year, consider the following activities:

1) Do a class study on how candidates use television. Have students pay special attention to televised debates, political ads, and interview programs. Some discussion questions include: *What kind of image does each candidate try to convey on television? Are the candidates running a positive campaign emphasizing how they can help their country, or do they rely on negative attacks on their opponents? Do the frequency and nature of the paid ads change as the election approaches? Are the candidates debating issues or does it seem to be an image dominated campaign?*

2) Have students keep track of where and when television ads appear. Discuss who political media experts hope to reach in different time slots (e.g., football game, popular family sitcom).

3) Ask students to take turns making a daily report on the candidates' activities of the preceding day based on newspaper, television, and radio news reports.

4) Your students will probably have their own presidential preferences based on who their parents favor. Give each faction—Democrats, Republicans, and independents—bulletin board space to promote candidates with posters, photographs, endorsements, and banners.

5) Have students (or groups) write questions they would ask one of the major candidates in an exclusive interview.

Answer Key

Introducing Presidential Elections (page 7)

1. every four years; on the first Tuesday after the first Monday in November
2. **candidate:** someone who seeks, or is nominated for, an office; a nominee
   primary: election in which members of a political party choose candidates to run for office in the general election
   nominee: person selected to run for public office; a candidate
   polls: places where votes are cast and counted
   inaugurated: sworn in office with a ceremony
   democratic: a form of government run either directly by the people or by their elected representatives
3. 5, 1, 6, 3, 4, 2
*4. Answers will vary.
**5. Answers will vary, depending on students' ages.
**6. Answers will vary, depending on the year.

Our Constitution Defines the Presidency (page 9)

1. (1) The legislative branch makes the laws.
   (2) The judicial branch explains, or interprets, the laws.
   (3) The executive branch sees that the laws are carried out.
2. Any three of the following: to enforce the Constitution and the nation's laws; to recommend measures to Congress; to sign into law or veto bills passed by Congress; to meet with leaders of other nations; to make treaties; to command the armed forces; to send troops into action; to appoint cabinet members, ambassadors, and federal judges.
3. be at least 35 years old; must have lived in the United States at least 14 years
4. two
5. the Constitution
*6. Answers will vary.
*7. Answers will vary.
**8. Traditionally, Presidents had served only two terms. Franklin Roosevelt broke the tradition by being elected for a third term in 1940 and a fourth term in 1944. Many Americans, especially Republicans, thought Roosevelt held the office too long and wanted to be certain that no president ever again served more than two terms.

The Electoral College (page 11)

1. no
2. a. electoral college; b. indirect; c. direct; d. winner-take-all
3. The 12th Amendment directed electors to vote separately for president and for vice president.
4. d
*5. Answers will vary.
**6. John Quincy Adams (1824)

The Electoral Map (page 13)

1. 270 votes
2. California (54), New York (33), Texas (32), Florida (25), Pennsylvania (23). Total: 167
3. Answers will vary according to state.

4. a. Minnesota has more people.
   b. 15
   c. 18
   d. 18
   e. 7
   f. Mia
*5. Answers will vary.
**6. John Quincy Adams (1824), Rutherford B. Hayes (1876), Benjamin Harrison (1888)

Who Can Vote? (page 15)

1. white men over 21 who owned property
2. **electorate:** the people who have the right to vote
   ratified: approved; confirmed
   poll tax: special tax, now illegal, that people in some states had to pay before they could vote
3. 14th Amendment–c; 15th Amendment–e; 19th Amendment–a; 23rd Amendment–b; 26th Amendment–d
4. people under 18, convicted felons, people who are severely mentally disabled
*5. Answers will vary.
*6. Answers will vary.
**7. Answers may include the following: the election of John F. Kennedy, our most youthful president, who inspired many young people to become politically active; the establishment of public service programs such as the Peace Corps and VISTA, through which large numbers of young people became socially active; the Vietnam War, for which 18-year-olds were drafted; the baby boom; the civil rights movement.

The Struggle for Women's Suffrage (page 17)

1. b, e
2. 42 years
3. equal rights in education, property, and voting
4. New York–c; Wyoming–b, Tennessee–a
*5. Answers will vary, but should include that women were now in the workforce doing what was considered as "men's work." Therefore, they felt they had proven themselves and should have the same political rights as men.
*6. Answers will vary, but should include that a woman's responsibility was in the home, caring for her husband and children; that women didn't understand politics or economics; that they weren't intelligent enough to make voting decisions.
**7. Answers will vary.

Political Parties (page 19)

1. Republican party and Democratic party
2. third
3. independents
4. no
5. Any three of the following: work in party's headquarters; call neighbors, hand out flyers; drive people to polling places
6. He feared that they would divide the nation and kindle animosity.

**7. Answers will vary, but should include that the Republican party was formed in the 1850s after Congress passed the Kansas–Nebraska Bill, which permitted slavery in these territories. Members of the Whig party who opposed the expansion of slavery formed the Republican party in 1854. Initially, almost all Republicans came from the North because most white southerners supported slavery.

8. Know-Nothing party: formed by Americans who resented new immigration in the 1840s. They were especially anti-Catholic and pro-slavery. **Prohibition party: their primary goal was to outlaw the making and selling of alcoholic beverages, but they also supported other economic and social reforms. In 1919, they succeeded in getting Congress to pass the 18th Amendment to ban alcohol. This amendment was later overturned.
Progressive party: generally supported social, political, and economic reforms supporting the interests of farmers and the working class. **Greenback party:** formed after the Civil War by farmers, the working class, and the poor who felt the government favored the wealthy. They asked the government to issue "greenbacks"—paper money not backed by gold or silver that would allow them to pay off their debts. **Free-Soil party:** formed in 1848 to support "free soil, free speech, free labor, and free men." **Bull Moose party:** formed in 1912 to protest the Republican party's renomination of William Taft. The name came from Roosevelt's announcement that he was ready to run against Taft because "I am fit as a bull moose."

**9. Answers will vary.

The Long Road to Victory (page 21)

1. to have already held a government office
2. **incumbent:** someone who holds a public office and is running for reelection
   debate: to formally discuss positions on issues
   landslide: an overwhelming majority of votes for one candidate or political party in an election
3. (from left to right) candidates announce; campaign for party nomination; win the nomination (or nominating conventions); campaign for election; election day
4. Answers will vary.
*5. Answers will vary.
**6. Reagan: governor of California
   Carter: governor of Georgia
   Nixon: member of Congress
   Kennedy: senator, member of Congress
   Eisenhower: none
   Bush: vice president to Ronald Reagan
   Clinton: governor of Arkansas

Presidential Primaries: The Race Is On! (page 23)

1. Primary elections do not fill an office; they measure voter support for candidates.
2. in late winter and spring of election year
3. e
4. They show they can attract voters, and this helps them raise campaign money; they give them committed delegates at the conventions.
5. New Hampshire
6. They have the largest populations, therefore, the most delegates.

*7. Answers will vary, but should include that Carter's unexpected victory in New Hampshire provided lots of publicity that helped him win other primaries.
*8. Answers will vary, but should include that by the time later primaries were held, many candidates dropped out because winners of early primaries seemed to have the nomination "sewed up." Therefore, those states' voters felt they didn't have much say in the nominating process.
**9. States without primary elections have caucuses. These include a series of meetings in which delegates are selected. At the state meeting, presidential candidates are chosen. Answers will vary by state.

Nominating Conventions: The Delegates (page 25)

1. political party
2. who to nominate for president and vice president, and what the party platform will be
3. **platform:** plan of action or statement of a national party's goals and views on important domestic and foreign policy issues
   plank: part of a political party's platform about a specific issue
   tradition: beliefs, opinions, or customs handed down from one generation to the next
4. 20
*5. Answers will vary.
*6. Answers will vary, but should include that now that conventions are televised, politicians and delegates want to appear more "civilized" in front of the cameras.
**7. Answers will vary, depending on the state and the results of the last election.

Nominating Conventions: The Events (page 27)

1. 3, 5, 1, 4, 6, 2
2. **keynote speaker:** person who gives the opening speech at a meeting
   seconding speech: speech giving additional support after the nomination of a candidate
   front-runner: the candidate with the best chance of winning
   over the top: during the counting of votes, the point at which a candidate has won the minimum number of votes necessary to win an election
3. F, T, F
*4. Answers will vary.
*5. Answers will vary, but should include that television stations must keep to their programming schedules. They also know that the American public has a short attention span and will easily become bored with long demonstrations.
**6. 1960: Democrats—John F. Kennedy and Lyndon B. Johnson; Republicans—Richard M. Nixon and Henry Cabot Lodge
   1972: Democrats—George McGovern and R. Sargent Shriver; Republicans—Richard M. Nixon and Spiro T. Agnew
   1988: Democrats—Michael Dukakis and Lloyd Bentsen; Republicans—George Bush and Dan Quayle
   1992: Democrats—Bill Clinton and Al Gore; Republicans—George Bush and Dan Quayle
   1996: Democrats—Bill Clinton and Al Gore; Republicans—Robert Dole and Jack Kemp

Notable Nominating Conventions (page 29)

1. **deadlock:** a tie that cannot be broken
   dark horse: an unexpected candidate about whom little is known; a person unexpectedly nominated for political office

2. **Across:** 2. candidate; 3. convention; 7. president; 8. plank; 10. speech
Down: 1. ballot; 4. vote; 5. nominate; 6. delegate; 7. platform; 8. party; 9. keynote
**3. Garfield, yes; Davis, no; Humphrey, no
**4. Senator Robert Kennedy
**5. Answers will vary.

The Running Mate (page 31)

1. F, T
2. to choose a running mate who has what the presidential nominee lacks
3. to win as many votes as possible
4. to preside over the Senate
*5. Answers will vary.
**6. John Tyler, Millard Fillmore, Andrew Johnson, James Garfield, Theodore Roosevelt, Calvin Coolidge, Harry Truman, Lyndon Johnson, George Bush
**7. Gerald Ford

The History of Campaigning (page 33)

1. F, F, T
2. **take the stump:** go out and make campaign speeches
whistle-stop campaign: early method of campaigning in which a candidate crossed the country by train and made speeches at each place the train stopped
transcontinental railroad line: a railroad line that goes from one end of the country to the other
3. Douglas–d; Bryan–e; McKinley–b; Hoover–f; Eisenhower–a; Reagan–c
4. Possible answers: railroad, airplane, radio, television, computer, telephone, fax machines
*5. Answers will vary.
*6. Answers will vary, but may include that computers give pollsters more sophisticated methods to determine voting patterns and identify donors. They make available both reliable and unreliable information about candidates. Many supporters now use the Internet to convince other citizens to vote for their candidates.
**7. John F. Kennedy and Richard Nixon (1960)

The Modern Campaign (page 35)

1. About two months, from Labor Day to election day
2. Any three of the following: shakes thousands of hands; makes speeches; talks on the phone; confers with political leaders; travels across the country; debates the issues with other candidates; hires political advisors, speech writers, and political media experts; gives interviews; holds press conferences; appears on radio and TV talk shows.
3. strategy–b; media–d; domestic–a; volunteer–c
4. A political media expert is hired to figure out how to reach the greatest number of voters through radio, television, and newspapers.
*5. Answers will vary, but may include: money, standings in the polls, debating other candidates, the work of staff and volunteers, and the campaign schedule.
*6. Answers will vary.
**7. Answers will vary.

Financing the Campaign (page 37)

1. one hundred ninety-three million four hundred thousand; $1.08
2. **finances:** money matters; system by which money is raised and managed
corruption: dishonesty; the use of unlawful means to tempt someone to do wrong
donors: people who give money to campaigns or causes
reform: change intended to improve conditions; improvement
3. c–$20 million
4. Any four of the following: campaign manager, media expert, press secretary, speech writer, hairdresser, doctor, fashion expert, campaign headquarters staff, attorney, accountant, finance director
*5. Answers will vary, but may include that young voters often look to these people as heroes and are likely to be influenced by them.
*6. Answers will vary, but may include that candidates spend lots of time raising money out of fear that their opponents will outspend them. Candidates who appeal to wealthy voters are probably more hurt by campaign spending laws than those who try to appeal to the "average voter."
*7. Answers will vary, but may include that professionals have common political interests and want to support candidates who share their interests.
*8. Answers will vary, but may include that many people worry that politicians' need to raise money will lead them to support programs and laws that are favorable to those who contribute large sums of money.

Public Opinion Polls (page 39)

1. An opinion poll is a survey of what the public thinks about candidates or issues.
2. So the poll will accurately reflect what all the public thinks.
3. f
4. The people they polled were not a cross section of all the population.
*5. The magazine's reputation for accuracy was ruined after it was wrong in predicting the outcome of the 1936 election.
*6. Answers will vary, but should include that Dewey felt that many of his supporters were so confident of his victory that they figured their vote wouldn't matter.
**7. Answers will vary.
**8. Answers will vary.

Campaigning by Television (page 41)

1. **underdog:** candidate or contestant considered unlikely to win
image: appearance; impression that a person, group, or organization presents to the public.
2. John F. Kennedy; Nixon debated well, but he looked pale, nervous, and tired.
3. The American public has broad exposure to candidates and issues.
However, television's emphasis on entertainment encourages candidates to focus on their images rather than issues. Also, because Americans rely so heavily on TV as their primary source of information, they often don't read in-depth articles about issues and candidates.
4. d
*5. Answers will vary.
*6. Answers will vary.
**7. Answers will vary.

Other Campaign Media (page 43)

1. Any three of the following: television, radio, newspapers, magazines, campaign materials
2. **editorial:** expressing the opinion of a newspaper or its editor
   slander: to say untrue things about or misrepresent someone, which results in damaging his or her reputation
   endorsements: statements of approval or support
   slogan: word or phrase used by a business, club, or political party to advertise its purpose; motto
3. newspaper and magazine articles
4. the editorial page
5. the bandwagon
6. glittering generality
*7. Answers will vary.
*8. Answers will vary.
**9. Answers will vary.

Election Day (page 45)

1. so people cannot influence or "buy" votes, or punish someone if they do not vote in a certain way
2. all the candidates' names are on the same ballot and voting is done in a closed booth
3. Check all items except: "put up campaign posters in polling places"
4. people assigned to polling places to make sure the election is run fairly
5. formal speeches by candidates announcing that they have lost the election
*6. Answers will vary, but should include that campaigning is forbidden so voters won't be pressured to change their votes.
*7. Answers will vary, but should include that it gives everyone a a chance to vote, including those who go after work.
**8. *Ballot* comes from the Italian word *ballotta*, which means "small ball." Centuries ago, people voted secretly by dropping a small ball in a box or other container. A white ball indicated a vote for something, a black ball indicated a vote against it. This is also where the term *blackballed* comes from.

Notable Elections (page 47)

1. Hayes had become President because of the decision of a commission of eight Republicans and seven Democrats.
2. Tilden only needed one more electoral vote to win. Twenty electoral votes were disputed because of fraud. Hayes thought he had lost. Congress appointed an electoral commission which consisted of seven Democrats, seven Republicans, and one independent. The independent had to resign and was replaced by a Republican judge. The vote was 8 to 7 to give all 20 disputed votes to Hayes.
3. It was the only election in which the candidate from a third party received more votes than a candidate from a major party.
4. calling an opponent names; Answers will vary.
5. a. T; b. R; c. W; d. W; e. T; f. R
**6. Bull Moose party
**7. Answers will vary.
**8. Answers will vary.

Inauguration Day (page 49)

1. January 20
2. lame duck
3. the inaugural address
4. the 20th Amendment
5. Thomas Jefferson–c; Abraham Lincoln–d; Franklin Roosevelt–b; John F. Kennedy–a
**6. Sample answer: Supporters felt the new president and the new Congress should begin their terms of office earlier because "lame duck" politicians don't usually get much government work done and the newly elected leaders are eager to start governing. Furthermore, they wanted to reduce the amount of time that a lame duck president could make appointments or sign laws that would go against the wishes of the new president.
**7. At the end of the eighteenth century tabulating votes took much longer and transportation was still slow and unreliable—especially in the winter months. Therefore, Inauguration Day was set for March to ensure enough time for the votes to be counted and for all memebers of the government to reach the Capitol from their home states. By the 1930's, the widespread use of trains and automobiles had greatly reduced the time it took to travel across the country.
**8. In an airplane en route from Dallas to Washington, D.C., Lyndon B. Johnson was sworn in as president of the United States following the death of President John F. Kennedy.

Should We Change the System? (page 51)

1. b
2. F, T, T, F
*3. Answers will vary.
*4. Answers will vary.
**5. Answers will vary, but may include that many Americans believe that their single vote won't make a difference in the outcome of an election, or that all politicians, no matter what their political party affiliation, are basically the same.
**6. Answers will vary.

The Presidents of the United States (page 56)

1. Seven presidents were elected from New York; answers will vary depending on state.
2. Franklin Roosevelt; he was elected for four terms.
3. William Henry Harrison and James Garfield
   Harrison died after he had been in office for three weeks. Garfield was assassinated during his first year in office.
4. Republicans: 21; Democrats: 20
5. Grover Cleveland
6. lawyers: 24; in Congress: 24; state legislators: 16; state governors: 17 (including William Henry Harrison, who was governor of the Indiana Territory); vice presidents: 14
7. Zachary Taylor, Ulysses S. Grant, William Taft, Herbert Hoover, Dwight Eisenhower
**8. Gerald Ford
**9. John Quincy Adams, Martin Van Buren, Grover Cleveland, Theodore Roosevelt, Herbert Hoover, Gerald Ford, Jimmy Carter

Bibliography

Archer, Jules. *Winners and Losers: How Elections Work in America*. Harcourt Brace Jovanovich, 1984.

Bailey, Thomas A., and David M. Kennedy. *The American Pageant*. D. C. Heath, 1979.

Boller, Paul F., Jr. *Presidential Campaigns*. Oxford University Press, 1984.

Coil, Suzanne M. *Campaign Financing: Politics and the Power of Money*. The Millbrook Press, 1994.

Congressional Quarterly. "Presidential Elections Since 1789." Third edition. Congressional Quarterly, 1983.

Corbin, Carole Lynn. *The Right to Vote: Issues in American History*. Franklin Watts, 1985.

Cunliffe, Marcus. *The American Heritage History of the Presidency*. American Heritage, 1968.

Gray, Lee Lerner. *How We Choose a President*. Fifth edition. St. Martin's Press, 1980.

Hargrove, Jim. *The Story of Presidential Elections*. Children's Press, 1988.

Henry, Christopher. *The Electoral College*. Franklin Watts, 1996.

___. *Presidential Conventions*. Franklin Watts, 1996.

___. *Presidential Elections*. Franklin Watts, 1996.

Hoopes, Roy. *Political Campaigning*. Franklin Watts, 1979.

Kownslar, Allan, and Terry Smart. *Civics: Citizens and Society*. Webster Division McGraw Hill, 1983.

The League of Women Voters Education Fund. *Choosing the President, 1984*. Schocken Books, 1984.

Lindop, Edmund. *The First Book of Elections*. Franklin Watts, 1968.

Lorant, Stefan. *The Glorious Burden: The American Presidency*. Harper & Row, 1969.

Modl, Tom, editor. *America's Elections: Opposing Viewpoints*. Greenhaven Press, 1988.

Pascoe, Elaine. *The Right to Vote*. The Millbrook Press, 1997.

Raber, Thomas R. *Presidential Campaign*. Lerner Publications, 1988.

Schlesinger, Arthur M. Jr. *Running for President: The Candidates and Their Images*. Simon & Schuster, 1994.

Schwartz, Alvin. *The People's Choice: The Story of Candidates, Campaigns, and Elections*. E. P. Dutton, 1968.

Silber, Irwin. *Songs America Voted By*. Stackpole Books, 1971.

Stein, Richard. *I Know America: Our Elections*. The Millbrook Press, 1994.

Weiss, Ann E. *News or Not? Facts and Feelings in the News Media*. E. P. Dutton, 1977.

Weiss, Ann E. *Party Politics, Party Problems*. Thomas Y. Crowell, 1980.

Weiss, Ann E. *Polls and Surveys: A Look at Public Opinion Research*. Franklin Watts, 1979.

World Book. *The World Book Encyclopedia*. 1985 edition.

CD Rom
Campaigns, Candidates and the Presidency. Compton's New Media, Inc., 1995.